Universal Wish

By

Greg S. Reid

Universal Wish by Greg S. Reid

Sherpa Press books may be purchased for educational, business, or sales promotional use.

For information, please write:
Special Markets
Sherpa Press
1621 Central Avenue
Cheyenne, WY 82001

First Edition

Library of Congress Cataloging-in-Publication Data
ISBN: 978-1-939078-01-8
eISBN: 978-1-939078-02-5

Universal Wish

By

Greg S. Reid

Contents

Foreword

A wish, like a dream, lives as long as it's believed in. It's a gift to teach our children to believe in those dreams no matter how impossible they seem. In a child's mind, everything is possible.

This imagination is an ability we all have, and yet, many of us lose it once we become adults, even teens. Whatever the dream, we still wish for success. Success is associated with financial freedom and fulfillment. It's a wish many people all over the world have and yet never obtain.

Universal Wish contains the essential insights and stories from extraordinary people who know how to turn dreams into reality. Beyond that, this book teaches the importance of showing others to do the same.

Many forget the most important aspect of gaining financial success, fulfillment and stability is giving back. By doing something that will benefit your community and the world you live in, you add more abundance to your life and create more wealth.

People today know what it means to be broke or to not have everything that they want or need. They know what it is to struggle. This is the time, when you can be a gift to someone in need.

Financial freedom is a possible dream. By applying the principles in these chapters with dedication and commitment to reach the goal, you will see an incredible difference in your life.

Use this book as inspiration and continue to believe in your dreams and help others make their dreams a reality, too!

Frank Shankwitz
Founder, Make-A-Wish Foundation

Chapter 1

BLOOMING

Hannah Braun stood and looked out the window of her midtown Manhattan office. Below her, people hurried down the sidewalk, talking into phones or staring straight ahead. She'd pick someone out of the crowd and imagine where they were going or what they were thinking. She drank coffee even though it was approaching late afternoon, and the sun was pulling further and further to the west. When she first moved to New York, she'd watch the sun set and pretend she could lasso it with a rope and let it pull her all the way back to California. To her parents, her older sister. To the familiar buildings, the familiar faces. Most importantly, to Conner. She let herself think about all of them, because she was trying not to think about the phone, and the fact that the one call she'd been waiting for had not yet arrived.

Her assistant, Brandon, sat cross-legged on the floor, a laptop balanced on his legs, a pensive look on his face. Even though the agency had hired Brandon almost six months ago, Hannah was still getting used to the idea of having an assistant. Brandon was a newly minted graduate from Columbia, fresh-faced and eager to learn all there was about the publishing industry. Hannah downed the rest of her lukewarm coffee and set the mug on top of a stack of precariously balanced manuscripts. Brandon looked up from the computer.

"Is there something going on that I don't know about? You planning on pulling an all-nighter? That's like your seventh cup of coffee."

She smiled faintly and resisted the urge to glare at the phone, as though a venomous enough look might actually make it ring.

"I didn't realize you were keeping track."

Brandon closed the laptop. "I'm almost done here," he said. "I just have to send that partial request for the middle grade novel and then I think you should let me take you out to Buttercup for some chocolate lava cake. You're supposed to drown your sorrows in chocolate, not caffeine."

But it wasn't sorrow she was feeling, not yet anyway. She'd signed a client, Victor Harwood, three months ago, after reading the memoir he'd written—with the help of his wife—in one sitting. It was called *Blooming* and it was about his life after he'd suffered a traumatic brain injury. It was poignant, heartfelt, and most importantly, it brilliantly illustrated the fact that if you were well supported, if you had the resources, anything was possible. Hannah had pitched the manuscript to editors she'd worked with before, and those she hadn't, and received passes from all but one.

Memoirs are difficult to place in today's market.

This is a lovely story but I don't know if I could sell it.

I loved it but the committee said no.

The list of reasons went on, all variations of the same theme. Before she had even pitched the manuscript, she'd made the decision she'd rent a car and drive all the way up to Washington County, to that little town in upstate New York where Victor and his wife, Mae, lived, in a house they had to remortgage after Victor's accident. She'd deliver the good news in person. *I sold your book. People will read your story. Your message will get out there.*

"Earth to Hannah!" Brandon waved both arms as though he were trying to get her attention in a large crowd from a far distance. "Chocolate lava cake—"

The phone rang.

Hannah's heart lurched. She grabbed the edge of her desk, the movement upsetting the stacks of manuscripts. The papers landed unceremoniously on the floor, but Hannah ignored them and took a deep breath. She picked up the phone.

"Hannah," the familiar voice said. It was Susan Fisher, the editor Hannah had sold her first bestseller to. Hannah was certain that even if everyone else passed, Susan would buy the manuscript. How could she not? "I'm so sorry," Susan continued. "It's a great story, it really is. But the economy is just not good for memoirs right now."

Susan kept talking, though Hannah no longer heard what she was saying. She hung up the phone and burst into tears.

At some point she became aware of Brandon standing next to her, a box of tissues in hand. She yanked one out and blew her nose, wiped at her eyes.

"I'm sorry," she said. She sat down in her chair and crushed the tissue in her hand.

"I take it Susan did not have good news."

"No, she did not."

"Sweetie." Brandon tilted her chin up. "You need a vacation. You work too hard. Take some time off. I know I may be a newbie on the literary agent scene, but anyone can see that you need a break. I can hold down the fort."

Hannah shook her head. "I can't take a vacation now." She gestured vaguely in the direction of her desk.

"Then you can at least let me take you out for some chocolate lava cake. No—I'll do you one better. Let me take you out tonight. I'm going to this thing, and you should come with me."

"Thing?"

"Yeah. A fundraising event for the Make-A-Wish Foundation. Frank Shankwitz is the keynote speaker. Come on. I'll tell you about it over chocolate lava cake."

They walked the three blocks to Buttercup and sat at a corner table. The chocolate lava cake came garnished with raspberries and Hannah picked at those. The sweet aroma of the cake was inviting but her stomach still felt twisted, her throat tight.

Brandon looked pointedly at her plate. "It's really best to eat it when it's still warm." His was halfway gone.

"Tell me more about this event," Hannah said.

"Well, you've heard of Make-A-Wish Foundation, right?"

"I have."

"I have twin cousins who have cystic fibrosis. They live up in Maine, in this tiny little town that's practically in Canada. They got to go to Disney World thanks to the Make-A-Wish Foundation. This was a while ago; I was maybe ten or eleven, I think. But I just remember being so inspired and grateful that there was this organization out there that could help make something like that happen. So I like going to these fundraising events when I can. I might be a poor post-college grad at the moment, but at some point in my life I'm hoping to be well-off enough to be able to do stuff like that for other people, too."

Hannah smiled. "That's awesome they were able to do that for your cousins."

"Yeah, it really was. They still say it's their favorite childhood memory." Brandon took the last bite of his cake and set his fork down. "Hannah, you better eat yours now or I'm going to."

She pushed the plate toward him. "Save me the last bite."

He folded his arms and leaned back in the chair. "Would you tell me something? Why are you taking this so hard? There are other editors you can pitch it to. And wasn't that one of the first things you told me when I started? That sometimes even a book you really love will never get to see the light of day."

She smiled wistfully and nodded. "Yes, I might've said something like that. And it is a good lesson to learn. Apparently I'm still learning it myself."

"It's definitely frustrating."

"And the manuscript went out to a lot of people. I know enough to know that if no one in this round picked it up, the chances of it happening in a second one are next to nothing."

Across the crowded café, a man caught her eye. He was tall, with tousled brown hair and the same easygoing smile Conner had. She stared at him for a moment and then looked at Brandon. "Okay," she said, sighing. "I'll tell you why that book is so important to me. I had a boyfriend in high school. Conner Tero. He was one of those people that everyone wanted to be around. Everyone wanted to be in class with him; wanted to hang out with him. He was so much fun. We had it all planned out, how we were going to move to New York after we graduated." She paused, a smile touching the corners of her mouth as she recalled the many late nights they'd stayed on the phone and talked about all the excellent adventures they'd have once they were out of their small town, away from their parents. "And then he was out skateboarding one night and got hit by a car. He wasn't wearing a helmet and at first the doctors were pretty sure he wasn't going to make it. But he did. And now—" Her throat constricted. "He's still in California. He lives at home, because it'd be really hard for him to live independently. He forgets things, has difficulty concentrating, sometimes he gets really bad headaches. So it'd be really difficult for him to hold down a job. And reading Victor's book reminded me of Conner in so many ways, and I know how much it would help him to hear a story like that, and I'm sure there's so many other people out there, too, that it could help."

The man who looked like Conner had stood up from his table and was walking to the exit. His arm encircled the lower back of the woman he was with, and though the woman was not as tall as Hannah and her hair was dark instead of blond, Hannah allowed herself to imagine that she was that woman and the man was indeed Conner. And instead of suffering a traumatic brain injury that left him forgetful and impatient, they had come out to New York like they'd planned, they had stayed together, they were living the life they'd been so certain would be theirs.

Brandon uncrossed his arms and ran a hand over his face. "Wow," he said. "I had no idea."

"I wouldn't expect you to; it's not something I've ever told anyone out here, actually."

"I'm really sorry, Hannah."

She stared at the chocolate cake on its white plate in the center of the table. She'd come to New York on her own because Conner had insisted; he'd told her he'd break up with her if she didn't. "It was our plan," he'd told her, on her last day as a resident of California. "And you can still follow through on our plan. Just … it'll be your plan now." So she went, even though she knew if the roles had been reversed, if it had been she who was unable to leave California, he would've stayed, regardless of the threats she made.

"Hannah, you're coming with me tonight," Brandon said. "Will you come with me? I think it'll be really good for you."

She agreed, even though all she really wanted to do was go home and draw the blinds, take a hot bath, and then go to bed.

Chapter 2

MOVE YOUR FEET

Hearing Frank Shankwitz speak had been more meaningful than she expected. As she stood there and listened to Frank talk about the little boy, Chris, who was the first child to be granted a wish, she couldn't help but think about Victor, whose book she hadn't been able to sell, and Conner, who she had left behind in California.

"Everyone has a universal wish," Frank had said in closing. "And discovering what that is, is one of the best things we can do for each other."

Brandon had introduced her to some of his friends, and she felt buoyant and inspired. What was her universal wish? What was it that she was supposed to be doing? Clearly she was in the wrong profession. Who was she really helping as a literary agent?

When the fundraiser was over, she followed Brandon toward the exit. As she said goodbye to all the new people she met, she noticed that her feelings of inspiration had started to ebb. The desire to do something was still there, though what had begun to overpower it was the crippling realization that she had no idea what it was she could do that could make a difference in anyone's life.

"Are you glad you came out tonight?" Brandon asked as they walked through the hotel lobby. "Isn't Frank great?"

Hannah brushed her hair back from her face and tried to ignore the uncertain feeling she felt in her chest. "He really is inspiring. And yeah, I had a good time. It's getting late, though."

"You want to share a cab?" Brandon held the door open for her and they stepped outside.

"No, it's okay. I'm going to walk," Hannah said.

"Are you sure?"

"Yeah. But thanks for bringing me, Brandon. I really did have a good time."

"I'm glad you did. And I still think you should consider taking a vacation. Even a short one." He gave her a quick hug. "Well, I'll see you tomorrow."

She watched as he walked to the edge of the sidewalk and hailed a cab. He got in and waved as they drove off, and Hannah waved back, though she remained where she was. She might've stayed there all night, rooted in that spot, if a man hadn't opened the door behind her.

"Oh, excuse me," he said.

Hannah started. "I'm sorry; I'm the one in the way." She turned and stepped out of the way and tried not to look flustered. "I … I … uh … "

The man smiled. “I’m Richard Muscio.” He was trim and attractive, with close-cropped salt and pepper hair. He had the sort of smile that a person couldn’t help but smile back at, and that’s exactly what Hannah did. “Did you enjoy the evening?”

“Yes and no. I mean, hearing Frank speak was awesome—especially after the day I had today. And I actually felt pretty inspired, but now … I don’t know what happened. I’m just standing here and I don’t know if I’m coming or going.”

“You want to take a little walk?”

Hannah paused. “Sure,” she said. “That’s probably better than just standing here blocking the doorway.”

They started walking. The October air was crisp but not quite cold yet. Hannah took a deep breath. “I’m sorry,” she said. “I’ve had a long day. I don’t usually make it a habit to just stand in doorways.”

“No need to apologize.”

“It’s just so weird, I felt really inspired after hearing Frank speak and I don’t know where that feeling went. I have a feeling that’s probably not a normal reaction.”

“I wouldn’t say there’s necessarily a right or wrong reaction. If you’re feeling confused about something though, don’t be afraid to examine it. Where is it coming from?”

“It’s coming from … it’s coming from … I have no idea where it’s coming from. I guess I’m just realizing how stuck I feel. But like inwardly stuck. I think to most people, it would probably look like I’m actually doing okay. Except I realized today that I’m not doing what I want to be doing.”

Richard nodded. "Can I give a little advice … I don't think you told me your name."

"Hannah."

"Hannah. You've got to move your feet. I mean that literally and figuratively. Get out in the community—it will make you a better person, it will make your community a better place. And I'm not saying it might not be uncomfortable at first, putting yourself out there. It very well might. But by putting yourself out there, meeting and talking with other people, volunteering with other people, you'll get clarity. It will give you a different perspective. It will help with your vision. Tell me about your vision."

Hannah shook her head. "I have no idea. I thought I knew what I wanted to do with my life, but now … I mean, hearing Frank speak makes me feel like there are so many possibilities, but that's almost more overwhelming than not knowing what to do. How do you decide? How do you choose?"

"Often times, it's less that you choose it rather than it chooses you. You'll just know. You might not know right away, but one day, the idea will just come to you."

"The thing is, I thought I knew. I thought this was it—living and working in New York. I grew up in California."

Richard smiled. "Yeah? That's where I'm from. I'm in town for the week, but I'll be heading back out there tomorrow. Where in California?"

"This little town just east of Santa Rosa."

"Beautiful area."

"It is. But it's so small, just this really small-town feel. Which is nice, in some ways, but all I ever wanted was to get away. To live somewhere where you could walk down the street and not recognize someone. Even when I'd go down to San Francisco I'd start seeing some of the same people. I just always dreamed of coming to New York."

"And you did."

"And I did. But now that seems like it's not enough. Or it was the wrong dream."

"Or maybe ... maybe it was just a part of your dream. One component of it. What is it that you do, if you don't mind me asking."

"I work in publishing. Literary agent. Which, to be honest, I had no idea even existed until I came out here and ended up getting an internship. I happen to love to read so it seemed like the dream job, but really, who else is it helping? It's the dream job for me in that I'm doing something I enjoy, but there are parts of it that aren't enjoyable and when that comes up I just don't know if I have it in me to see it through to the good stuff again. And it's not about the money," she added. "I mean, I'm not upset because I'm not making money. I guess I want to find something that I'll feel just as enthusiastic about in the good times *and* the bad. That seems crucial, actually."

"You're absolutely right—it is. But in the meantime, one of the best things you can do is put yourself out there. When you participate, when you're really interested in life but are coming from a place of non-judgment, that's what's going to give you clarity. You'll be able to see how your life evolves."

They'd reached the entrance to the subway. "This is me," Hannah said. She smiled at Richard. "Thanks so much for walking with me. I actually feel a lot better. Maybe our paths will cross again in California some time. I try to go back when I can, to see my family and friends."

"That'd be great. Are you heading out there for Thanksgiving?"

"I don't know. I haven't figured that out yet. That would probably be a good idea though, since it's been a little while since I last went back."

"Well, I know it's not exactly in the same neighborhood, but if you're near Oceanside, come down to the Turkey Trot."

Hannah smiled. "What's that?"

"It's an annual road-race fundraiser we hold on Thanksgiving. It's a lot of fun. You'll get to meet a lot of great people. You should check it out if you're around."

"Maybe I will. My sister lives in San Diego, actually. And she's into running; I'll have to ask her if she's ever done it. She was always trying to get me to go running with her when we were younger but it just wasn't my thing."

"Well, you can also walk it, too. Plenty of people do." He smiled at her again and reached out and patted her shoulder. "Just remember to move your feet."

Chapter 3

MAKE YOUR OWN PIE

She got off the subway at Eighth and Broadway and started to walk to her apartment. It was getting late and she planned to be in the office early tomorrow, but as she passed by Ellie's Coffee Shop, she decided to go in. She was hungry. More than that, though, she didn't feel like being alone in her apartment just yet.

"Sit wherever you'd like," a waitress called out as she hurried by with a coffee pot. "I'll be with you in a sec."

Hannah stood in the doorway for a moment and surveyed the options. There were several booths open in the back but then her eyes landed at the counter, where a few patrons sat atop maroon vinyl stools.

"I'm just going to sit over here," she said to the waitress as she retreated back.

She settled in on one of the stools and picked up the plastic-encased menu. Ellie's served breakfast all day but Hannah didn't feel like pancakes or eggs benedict. She wasn't sure what she wanted. She sighed and set the menu down.

"You want coffee, honey?" the waitress asked as she walked around the counter.

"Decaf, please."

"And what else?"

"Um … give me a minute." Hannah looked back down at the menu, the words an incomprehensible jumble in front of her eyes. She had no idea what she wanted.

"Get the apple pie," the man seated next to her said.

Hannah looked at him. "Excuse me?"

He gestured to his own plate in front of him. "Best in the house."

"Well then, I guess I'll get the apple pie," she said to the waitress. She turned to the man. "Thanks for the tip. I actually live nearby and come here often but I've never ordered the apple pie."

"That's the thing about pie—you can't go wrong with it. Now if only everyone could learn to make their own, we'd all be in pretty good shape, wouldn't we?"

Hannah stirred some cream into her coffee. "I don't know how to make pie. I can barely cook pasta."

"But that's probably because you've never actually took the time to learn how to make a pie, correct?"

"I guess so, yeah."

"I'm sure you're familiar with the story of the Little Red Hen."

"I am."

"Well, it's like that. Nobody wants to participate in putting something together, but they all want to participate in the end result. The good stuff. I wish everyone would learn to make their own pie. With a little bit of proper thinking and correct education, people can learn to make their own pies and have as much pie as they want."

Hannah took a tentative sip of her coffee, which was still too hot. The waitress set down a plate in front of her.

"Need anything else, honey?" she asked, snapping her gum.

"No, thank you," Hannah said. She took a bite of the apple pie. "Wow," she said, looking back over at the man. "You were right. This is amazing. Although I don't think I'd ever be able to make anything this good."

"That's just not true." He laughed and held out his hand. "I'm Rick Kvalheim."

"Hannah Braun." She took another bite. The tartness of the apples, combined with the brown sugar and cinnamon, coalesced perfectly. There was a scoop of vanilla ice cream next to the pie, but she ignored it and enjoyed the pie on its own. "So, when you say pie, in terms of people making their own, you're talking about life, aren't you? Or something along those lines."

"I am."

"I went to this fundraiser tonight and heard Frank Shankwitz speak. The guy who started the Make-A-Wish Foundation. It was really eye-opening for me. Kind of along the same lines as this—having a wish and doing something to actualize it." She set her fork down and took a sip of coffee. "But let me ask you something, Rick."

He smiled. "Please."

"Since you seem pretty knowledgeable about the subject, maybe you can give me some advice. How do you know? How is someone supposed to know what kind of pie they want to make?"

"That's a great question. How are you supposed to know? Well, think of pie as your sweet spot in life. Is life the way you want it to be? Yes? Good. If it's not, are you actively working to get it there? That's good, too. The most important thing, Hannah, is to be clear about your outcome. What is it you're actually trying to do? Once you've figured that out, you need to assemble the know-how to make it happen. Either you need to become educated or you need to find team members that know how that works. It's a team sport. So you've got to go about finding the right members for your team. You need to make a plan and assemble the team to execute that plan. And then you need to assess the outcome, and, if necessary, you need to make adjustments or improvements in order to get the job done.

"Do you have a dream, Hannah?"

"I did once," she said, thinking back to her late night phone calls with Conner and how spectacular and certain their future seemed to be, and how she'd thought it was almost just as much fun to talk about it as it would be to actually live it.

"Well, this whole country once had a really great collective dream. But these days, it seems like the new American Dream is to just get by. So you've got people going around asking themselves, *Am I going to drown or am I going to survive? If I hang onto enough people, maybe we can all float together.* But you know what? There's no joy in that."

"It really is about finding your joy, isn't it?" Hannah set her spoon down on the edge of her plate. "That's what I feel like I need to do now. Find that joy. But it might not turn out to be that easy."

"Oh, I know. No one ever said it's going to be easy. But it's worth it, wouldn't you say? I mean, think about the time it takes to actually make a pie. It's actually a fairly labor-intensive process, what with cutting the apples, making the crust, et cetera. Then you have to wait for it to bake, but then … if you've put in the effort and done things the way they're supposed to be, you've got this really great thing to enjoy."

"As opposed to just going down to the supermarket and buying one?"

"Well, that works, too. Except instead of doing the work yourself, you've paid your supermarket team to ship the pies that were made by some other team into your supermarket so you can go down there and buy one."

Hannah looked down at her plate, which was all but scraped clean. "And it probably wouldn't be as good as this, huh?"

Rick lifted his coffee cup to her. "You got that right."

Chapter 4

A NATURAL GIFT

Hannah was in the office early the next morning, despite having slept little the night before. After she'd said goodnight to Rick, she walked the four blocks to her apartment. She'd poured herself a glass of wine and ran a hot bath, then replayed the events of the night in her head. She was tempted to call Brandon and thank him, but by then it was approaching midnight.

Now, she sat at her desk and tried to call forth some of the inspiration she'd felt last night. Wasn't it funny, she thought, how she'd just met those two men who had been so generous in sharing their wisdom with her. She normally wasn't one to strike up conversations with complete strangers, but it had seemed right.

She sipped her latte and then swiveled her office chair around and looked out the window. The city was awash in the pale yellow light of an early morning sun. Below her, people hurried down the sidewalk. She wondered how many of them were joyful, how many knew how to make their own pies.

She turned back to her desk, glancing at the wall clock. She needed to make a phone call, but she told herself it was still too early. Instead, she started to read through her emails. She received anywhere from thirty to seventy-five queries per day, all of which she read, though she only personally responded to the ones which sounded intriguing. The rest, Brandon sent form rejections to, which said:

Dear Author,

Thank you for considering us for your project. Hannah has reviewed your material and unfortunately, this does not seem right for our list. We wish you the best of luck.

Sincerely,

Brandon Davies
Assistant to Hannah Braun

Hannah opened an email, read the query and knew right away that this was a first novel. Still, she glanced over the sample pages and then hit the reply button.

Dear Bill, she wrote.

Thank you for sending me your query and sample pages. The premise sounds intriguing, but I can tell from the short bit I read that this is still an early draft and not as polished as it could be.

Clearly, you are passionate about your work, and while I fully appreciate the level of dedication it takes to complete a novel, yours is not quite ready yet. Give it some time, polish it the best you can, and then feel free to re-query me.

Warm regards,

Hannah Braun

She spent the morning typing a personalized response to each query she received. By the time lunch rolled around, she'd responded to twenty-four of the sixty new queries she'd received yesterday.

"You want me to grab you a sandwich or anything on my way back from lunch?" Brandon asked.

"No, that's okay," Hannah said. She stretched, feeling something in her back crack. "I'm going to head out after I make this phone call. I need to stretch my legs. Thanks for offering though."

Brandon nodded and started to walk out the door. He stopped. "You know, I think it's really cool that you're responding to these queries. Maybe not the smartest thing time-wise, but you're really giving hope to a lot of writers out there. That's pretty awesome."

Hannah smiled. "Thanks, Brandon."

She waited a minute after he left before picking up the phone. She took a deep breath and then dialed.

"This is Hannah Braun calling for Victor," she said when someone picked up.

"Hi, Hannah! It's Mae. Hold on; let me get Victor."

Hannah could hear the giddiness in the woman's voice and she felt her stomach sink. She stood up and leaned on the edge of her desk.

"Hello, Hannah," Victor said a moment later. "Mae and I were just talking about you last night at supper. Mae said she was pretty sure you'd be calling us soon with good news. She knows things like that, sometimes. Knows things ahead of time."

Hannah forced a smile. "Hi, Victor," she said. "Actually … I'm afraid I'm calling with some bad news."

There was a pause. "It's okay, Hannah," he said. "Whatever it is. You sound so sad. Is … is no one interested in my book?"

"I heard back from the last editor yesterday. They've decided to pass. I'm so sorry. There are other editors I can pitch the book to. But I wanted to keep you updated and let you know where we stood right now."

"I heard someone say once their book was like their baby," Victor said, speaking slowly. "Their child. It didn't really make a whole lot of sense to me at the time, but that's just 'cause I'd never written a book. And Mae and I kind of feel like this book is our child, and … and it doesn't feel good if people are out there telling you your child's no good."

"Victor—"

"I think we'd rather you not submit it to anyone else. At least not right now. We know you believe in the story,

Hannah. And if it never gets published, well, that's okay, too. We know you did your best."

When Hannah hung up the phone, she sat perched at the edge of her desk and stared off into the middle distance. So that was it. She understood where Victor was coming from, and regardless of what he said, she knew she'd failed him. His story would never get out there.

She grabbed her purse and her jacket and left the office. She walked a few blocks and then veered into a café where she ordered tea and a turkey sandwich. She sat at a corner table and tried not to let Victor's voice echo through her mind. What was she doing? What had she been talking about last night, with Richard Muscio and Rick Kvalheim? And what about hearing Frank speak, hadn't that spoken to some part of her that she hadn't even realized existed? She was horrified to feel her eyes filling with tears, but it was beyond the point of her control. Through her blurred vision, she saw the man at the next table watching her, which only added to her mortification. She was not the type of girl to just start crying, least of all not in a public place. Certainly not in some crowded café surrounded by strangers.

"Is everything okay?" the man asked.

"I'm sorry," Hannah said. She wiped at her eyes and wished she had something more than the sleeve of her sweater. "I don't know what's wrong with me."

The man stood up, smiling at her. He was young, with dark hair and kind eyes. He gestured to the empty seat in front of her. "May I?"

"I think the only thing more horrifying than actually crying in public is having someone I don't know sit with me while I do so, but … sure." She sniffled.

"My name's Jason Munson."

"I'm Hannah."

"Well, now we know each other, Hannah, so you don't have to feel bad about crying in front of someone you don't know."

Hannah pulled one of the scratchy napkins from the dispenser and blotted her face. "I'm so embarrassed. I'm sorry."

"You don't have to keep apologizing. I actually think it's a really powerful thing when people cry in public."

She crumpled the napkin up and held it in her hand. "You do?"

"Yeah, I do. I know most people view that as a weakness, but really, I think it's a fantastic strength. You shouldn't be embarrassed. What were you thinking about right then?"

"I … I don't know. Everything. Nothing. I just feel like I'm at this point where I have no idea what I'm supposed to be doing. Except I've got this career that I thought I wanted, and it's actually going pretty well, but … it's not making me feel the way I thought it would. I'm a literary agent. And I signed this client who had written an amazing book. I loved it. Part of the reason I loved it was because it's personally relevant to me. It's this man's story about his life after a traumatic brain injury. And my boyfriend in high school got into an accident and suffered a head injury, and I was thinking about him, too, and that book, and everything seems so overwhelming and pointless all at the same time." Hannah blew her nose in the napkin. "And now here I am unloading all this on you. I'm sorry."

"You really don't need to keep apologizing; you're fine. You're doing fine. Everything is going to be okay."

"I'd really like to believe that."

"What is your gift? What is it that you'd say you're good at?"

"I . . . I don't know. You're kind of putting me on the spot."

"It's really important for people to discover what their gifts and talents are. That might seem obvious, but you'd be amazed the number of people that are doing things not because they've got an aptitude for it but because they feel like it's just what they've got to do. Trying to be a jack-of-all-trades might sound like a good idea, but it prevents you from getting really good at any one thing. No one is good at everything. You'd be better served to focus your energy, and it's so much easier to focus your energy on something you're good at. Everyone's got a natural fit for something. Sometimes it can be difficult to know what that is. But it's worth it to find out. You said you're a literary agent?"

"Yes."

"So that right there tells me you like to read. And that you also must know what makes a good story, and what other people like to read. You're probably pretty good at understanding what is of interest to other people. A lot of the time, when we have a natural gift, we don't appreciate it.

Because you're born with it and didn't have to do anything to get it, it's easy to take it for granted. And if you're not exactly sure what your gift might be, try looking at where you're already producing results."

"Okay." Hannah nodded. "I like helping people, which is a totally generic answer, right? But I really, truly find pleasure in helping people. And where I'm producing results with that—most of the time—is discovering new authors. Two of my debut authors have had best sellers. I love helping them get their work out there, because I know it's a path they want to take. It's such a great feeling to sign a client who's been working tirelessly on a manuscript for years and years. Doing it because it's a true labor of love. And I get to be a part of that, I get to help them do what they love."

"Well there you go." Jason smiled. "And here you are thinking you didn't have any natural talents. It sounds like to me you've got plenty."

After lunch, Hannah went back to the office. Brandon sat on the couch in the lounge area outside her office, laptop balanced on his knees. "Should I start responding to queries again?" he asked.

"Yes. I've got to make a few phone calls. But first, why don't you rewrite the rejection form we send out. I think it could be … friendlier. More encouraging."

"Of course," he said.

Hannah closed her office door. She threw her purse down and went and sat behind her desk. She picked up the phone and dialed the numbers she knew by heart.

"Hi, Mrs. Tero," she said when the familiar voice answered. "It's Hannah."

"Hannah!" Mrs. Tero sounded genuinely happy to hear from her. Hannah let out a breath. "How are you? I feel like it's been a while since we last heard from you; what is new in your life? Actually, hold on one sec." There was a muffled sound and Hannah could hear Mrs. Tero speaking but couldn't understand what she was saying. "Okay, I'm back," she said. "That was Conner. I told him he'll have a chance to speak to you but I wanted a few minutes first! So what is new?"

They chatted for a little while and then Conner got on the line.

"Hannah," he said. She could hear the smile in his voice. "Hey, babe."

He still talked to her in the easy way he always had, even right after the accident when he was coming off all the medication and was confused and didn't seem to recognize anyone but her.

"Hi," she said. "How are you doing? I wanted to hear your voice."

"Things are okay. I don't know if Mom told you or not but I started doing this riding program at the junior college. It's actually been a lot of fun. I never really considered myself a horse guy, but in a way, it's not so much different than a skateboard." He laughed. "Maybe one of these days I'll get good enough to do some jumps."

"That's great," she said. She knew how difficult it was for him to be sedentary, to not be able to get out there and be active the way he used to. "I'm really happy to hear that."

"So how is city life? Fill me in. All the details."

"I know it's been a little while since we talked. But I signed this client, this guy Victor. He wrote a memoir about his life after a skiing accident. It really … it made me think of you. He's doing really well now, though. He's living a full, happy life."

"Hannah Braun, you're not starting to feel bad for me, are you? That's sort of what it sounds like."

"No. It just reminded me of you because I saw a lot of similarities. But at the same time, you're not living a really full life, are you? Would you say that?"

"I don't know. Is life like a shopping bag we're supposed to fill up with stuff? But we don't have to talk about that now, do we? I'd rather hear about what's new with you."

She smiled. "Okay. Where are you right now?"

"I'm on the deck. Lying on the lounge chair. The sun is shining."

"That sounds nice."

"It is. So really, how is New York?"

"Good. I went to this fundraiser a few days ago with my assistant, and Frank Shankwitz was speaking. He's the guy who started the Make-A-Wish Foundation. And hearing him speak was really awesome. It made me want to do something. Something different than what I'm doing now."

"Yeah? Like what?"

"I don't know. That's the part I still need to figure out."

"Well, you will. I know you will."

"Thanks. Do you guys have Thanksgiving plans?"

"The usual, I'm sure. Why? Thinking of crashing?"

"You know, I just might. Did you know there's a road race down in Oceanside held on Thanksgiving Day? The Turkey Trot?"

"I didn't know. Does Kate run in it?"

"She might. I was actually going to give her a call after I got off the phone with you."

"Never get off the phone with me. I'm just kidding. But it would be great to see you, Hannah. I wouldn't mind seeing you again one bit."

She smiled. "I'm sure you wouldn't. Maybe that can happen. I've got a lot of vacation time accrued. I'll see what I can do."

After she hung up with Conner, she called her sister, Kate.

"Have you ever heard of the Turkey Trot?" she asked.

"Of course! I've done it the past two years now. This way I can feel less guilty about stuffing myself silly with that pecan pie Scott's mother makes. Why do you ask?"

"I met Richard Muscio the other night."

"Oh really? I've only met him once, but he seems really great. Well, what are your Thanksgiving plans? You should come out here and run it with me."

"You know, I'm actually thinking about taking some time off and doing that. Coming out to California. It's been awhile. I'll go up and stay with Mom and Dad and then get down there for a few days. I could use a break, to be honest."

"Is everything okay?"

Hannah could see her sister clearly, see her standing there in her kitchen or out on the deck, folding her arms across her chest, a slight frown on her face. Her sister was tall and blond, lighter blond than Hannah, but when they were growing up people often mistook them for twins. Hannah had always felt a burst of pride whenever anyone had made the error, and it was always Kate who informed them she was actually the older sister.

"Yeah, everything's fine. I heard Frank Shankwitz speak last night at this fundraiser. That's where I met Richard. It was really eye opening. But … I'll tell you more about it when I see you."

"So you're definitely coming then?" Her sister's voice came through the phone so clearly it was like she was sitting right there, in person.

Hannah twirled the phone cord around her finger. "Yes," she said. "I'll be there."

Chapter 5

COMING TOGETHER

Once Hannah made the decision to go back to California, she found that was all she could think about. Her last trip had been almost three years ago, and now that she'd booked the tickets, arranged for a car rental, and informed her family and friends, she couldn't believe she'd managed to stay away for so long.

The weekend before she was to leave, she dug out a pair of yoga pants and found her seldom-worn New Balances. She threw on a sweatshirt, tied her hair back, and headed up to Central Park. She hadn't decided if she'd spend Thanksgiving with her sister or at her parents' house, but she figured it'd be good to at least attempt a lap around the park.

"Keep your feet moving," she said to herself as she stepped outside.

It was one of those gray mornings where the clouds seemed as thick as a tabletop. Dead leaves skittered around her feet. She walked past newsstands, a bookstore, several coffee shops. She glanced down a narrow alley and saw clothes hung out to dry on the fire escape. Steam billowed out from one of the manhole covers and the air felt cool and damp. She passed a nondescript brick building with a simple wooden sign above the door: *The Women's Resource Center.* Somehow, she'd never noticed it before. A plastic brochure holder was affixed to the wall, and Hannah took one of the brochures out. She scanned the list of programs, which included counseling, career and legal services, classes, childcare, groups, and housing support. She folded the brochure and stuck it into the front pocket of her sweatshirt, then continued on her way.

When she got to Central Park, she tried running for a little bit but stopped when her right knee started to ache. She thought of what Jason Munson had said to her, to try to find your natural gifts. She wasn't a runner so there was no point in trying to force herself to be one. Instead, she slowed to a leisurely stroll and let herself take in all the sights she'd missed because she was usually in such a hurry to get wherever she was going.

She was up near East Meadow when she saw a couple sitting together on one of the benches, holding coffee cups and laughing about something. They sat with their bodies turned toward each other, the man's right knee touching the woman's left knee. They had an easy, comfortable way about them. Hannah felt a twinge. She'd been out on a few dates since coming to New York, but nothing serious. Mainly, she told herself, because she didn't have the time. But the truth of it was, no one could captivate her the way Conner had, and being with someone else just didn't seem right.

"Hi there," the man said as she went past. Hannah blushed and considered just continuing on; she was certain they'd seen her staring but she stopped and returned his smile.

"Hello," she said, exhaling.

"Are you enjoying your walk?" the woman asked.

"I am," she said. "I'm usually so busy going from one place to the next that I don't actually get to take in the sights. Even if it's not a gorgeous sunny day out." She looked up at the gray-filled sky. "How is your day going?"

"Better than extraordinary," the man said. "That's how my day starts, and that's how it ends every single day."

"That's amazing!" Hannah said.

"The best part is I get to spend it with the most beautiful girl in the world, we don't get too much down time together, so when we can squeeze in a few moments here and there, we make the most of it."

"You guys seem really happy together," Hannah said. "I really noticed that when I was going by. You guys are lucky."

"We make our own luck," the woman replied with a smile. "Do you have someone special in your life?"

"Like a boyfriend? No, not really. I did, a while ago but …" Hannah trailed off. "I'm going out to California to see him next week, actually."

"That's great that you're still in touch," the woman said. She held out her hand. "I'm Christine, by the way. And this is my husband."

"Brad Alt," the man said, offering his hand after Hannah shook Christine's.

"Hannah Braun. Nice to meet you guys. Would you mind … would you mind if I asked you a question?"

"Ask away," Christine said.

"Well … how do you do it? I mean, you guys just look really happy together. It's inspiring, really." Hannah smiled to herself. "I feel like I've been meeting a lot of inspiring people lately. It's been pretty awesome, actually. I've been thinking of making some changes in my life."

"Really? That's wonderful," Christine said. "Making changes can be hard. But isn't it amazing how once you make the choice all these new possibilities start opening up?"

"Yeah, I guess you're right," Hannah said. She stuck her hands in the sweatshirt pocket and felt the folded up brochure. "I actually have this idea," she said. "It's been kind of percolating the past few weeks now, but … " She paused. What was she doing, standing here talking to two complete strangers about some crazy idea she'd dreamed up that would probably never come to fruition? But Brad and Christine were both looking at her with interest, like they really did want to hear whatever it was she was about to say. "I currently work in a very for-profit industry," she continued. "But I've been thinking that I'd like to change that. I'd like to do something else. My idea was to start a nonprofit center that helps people with traumatic brain injuries live independent lives." She smiled as she heard herself say it out loud.

"That's something you feel passionate about, isn't it?" Brad asked.

"Yes," Hannah said. "I do. It's … it's kind of a personal connection. That boyfriend I had. The one I'm going to visit in California … he's actually kind of why I got this idea in the first place. He was in a skateboarding accident and I saw firsthand how having a traumatic brain injury just completely changed his life."

"That must've been really difficult," Christine said.

"It was. Is. We had all these plans to move out to New York, to just be together and enjoy each other, and yeah, I know we were young, but we'd talked about having a family at some point." Hannah laughed. "Way far in the future, of course. I guess I kind of always thought we'd have … we'd have what you guys have."

"Whatever you want in life you can have," Brad said. "It all starts with a dream. Once you have your dream, start filling in all the details of exactly how you want everything to be. Make a plan on how you could make your dream a reality, then immediately take one small step towards achieving that dream."

"I guess that's where I'm at now," Hannah said. "And not even the planning yet; I'm still at the dream part."

"That's ok," Brad said. "That's exactly where you want to start. Most people think to get anything they want in life it will simply just show up. That's not how life works; life will give you everything you want, but first you have to be clear on what you want. Then life will test you to see if you are worthy of receiving the gift. This is what I call challenges, and the bigger the reward, the bigger the challenge. It's simple, it's not going to be easy, but it will be worth it."

"I think it's great that you're thinking about doing this," Christine said. "It seems like a lot of people just end up getting stuck in these jobs or careers they thought they wanted but realize later they really don't. And then they find themselves in this cycle of unhappiness that can be terribly hard to extricate yourself from. Change can be really scary, but it's essential. Especially if what you're doing isn't serving you in a positive way. I want people not just to exist, but to live." Christine smiled. "And to help improve the lives of everyone they come in contact with, whether it be with a smile or a kind gesture. Through all the challenges and opportunities that have come my way, it's helped shape my character and make me a stronger person. In order to do that, you've got to conquer these challenges and find an empowered meaning for each opportunity that you're faced with. One of the best things you can do is to work on yourself. So you definitely want to start working on yourself, even if it's something small, something as simple as a smile. You'll notice your life starts to become very full of all the little things that we seem to overlook. Small steps. If you try to do everything all at once it can seem very overwhelming. But if you break it down into little steps and you start establishing habits, that will then help you grow and conquer the different things that come your way."

"I like the idea of little steps," Hannah said, nodding. "That makes it sound much more doable. Not so overwhelming."

"One of the first things you can do is self-educate. Read books, listen to the recordings of those that want to share their wisdom. Find things that are meaningful to you, that will help you grow, and maybe even keep a journal. Write down what you want to accomplish in life, both the short-term goals and the long-term ones."

"You kind of answered my question I originally wanted to ask you," Hannah said. "About how you guys were able to be so happy together. I feel like you can apply everything you just told me not just to starting a business but also to being in a relationship, which I guess having a business is kind of like, huh?"

"Exactly," Brad said. ""Our relationship is like a garden. To make it beautiful you must take care of it, nurture it and constantly pull out the weeds. It takes work! All gardens get weeds, but if you pull the weeds out when they're small they won't get too big. If the weeds get too big they will eventually take over your garden. Take time to enjoy life, it's not the things in life that make us happy, it's the experiences we have along the way that are valuable."

"I always wanted a family. I mean, I know I'm still young, but I'd love to have what you guys have."

Christine smiled at her. "You will, Hannah. It doesn't always happen right away, or when you want it to, but you're certainly on the right path."

"It was really great to meet both of you. Thanks for talking with me. I'll let you get back to enjoying your day."

"Nice to meet you, too." They waved as Hannah turned to leave, and she thought about how some day, if she worked at it, she would be able to have something similar to what they did.

Chapter 6

BACK TO THE BASICS

Hannah had never been particularly fond of flying or navigating her way through an airport. Everyone seemed to be in a rush, irritated or sleep-deprived. It was like the city, only concentrated within the confines of a building.

Arriving at the airport always reminded her of the day she left California, flying out of SFO, by herself, instead of with Conner. He'd wanted to come to the airport with her and see her off but she wouldn't let him. She hadn't been sure she would've been able to actually get on the plane if he'd been there, waving goodbye.

This morning, though, she felt excited and found herself smiling at people as they hurried by her. She pulled her carry-on Samsonite behind her, the only thing she'd brought, other than her purse, though she'd been tempted to pack her laptop and a few client manuscripts as well.

The line through security zigzagged around the aisles created by the barriers. A very pretty woman and her even prettier daughter stood a few people in front of Hannah, each carrying Louis Vuitton handbags. The woman kept turning around, looking for someone over Hannah's shoulder. A few minutes later, a man pushed past Hannah and stood next to the woman. He was tall and square-shouldered with an air of authority.

"It turns out," he bellowed in a supercilious voice as though addressing everyone within earshot, "that being a federal judge means you must go through security like everyone else." The woman smiled and smoothed his lapels down, saying something to him that Hannah couldn't quite make out. The girl, though, shifted her purse to her other shoulder and rolled her eyes.

"Duh, Daddy. Now everyone knows what you do!" she said sarcastically and equally as loud, as if embarrassed yet maintaining superiority with her Dad's actions and position.

The line inched forward.

The woman directly behind Hannah laughed softly to herself. Hannah turned and the woman met her gaze. "He seems rather proud of himself, doesn't he?" the woman murmured.

Hannah looked back to the judge, who was now tapping his foot and making a show of looking at the large gold watch on his wrist. Hannah laughed too, and wondered if the man had any idea how silly he was coming across.

"He does," she said. "Though I don't know if that's something to be proud of."

"Can you imagine how different relationships would be if people didn't have feelings of entitlement? What the world might be like? It's funny, I was just talking about it with my kids this morning. Then, here I am four hours later witnessing this behavior. I can't help feeling sad for him or anyone who feels the need to announce to everyone how important he or she is."

"I agree," Hannah said. She held out her hand. "I'm Hannah."

"Joan Magill. Where are you headed today?"

"California. I took a little time off from work and I'm going to visit my family."

"Well, that's lovely. I'm sure your family will be thrilled to see you."

"I think they will. I'll be glad to see them, too. I'm glad for a break from work—I did not bring a single work-related thing with me. I even left my laptop."

"I'm impressed. How nice to make your family the priority! It's amazing how plugged in we are these days, isn't it?"

"Yes. And how you don't even realize it until some natural disaster comes and knocks out the power supply for the day."

"Well, I look at those situations as opportunities to get back to the basics," Joan said. "Technology is wonderful and it certainly allows us to do a myriad of tasks we wouldn't be able to do otherwise. However, like you said, Hannah, when there's a big storm that knocks the power out for a day or two it seems like a huge adjustment: no TV, no internet, no hot water, and unless you have a gas stove, no cooking. People have to find other ways to survive and creative means to entertain themselves. Many times that relates back to the most essential of basics, people relating to other people. Then when the power gets restored, while it was an inconvenience, I believe many people reflect back to that day or two they went without and realize there was a calmness, slowness, a bonding of coming together that probably wouldn't have happened otherwise. Everyone's in such fast motion today and with the vastness and anonymity of the internet, it seems people have gotten to the point where they don't care as much about other people. So, going back to the basics is good, it gives one clarity."

"You're absolutely right," Hannah said. "Even what we're doing right here. Normally, if I were standing in line next to someone, I'd be on the phone or texting someone or doing something work-related. I probably wouldn't just be striking up a conversation with the person next to me."

"What do you do for work?"

"I'm a literary agent. But lately, I've been thinking about doing something else. In fact, it's a little like what you said with the whole idea of back to the basics. I want to do something that's more meaningful than just helping people find their next great read. Not that there's anything wrong with that, of course; I just don't think it's the right thing for me to be doing anymore."

"It is so refreshing to hear you say that! I am a firm believer that anyone can accomplish whatever it is they set out to do. You've got to create your own pathways. It may not be easy but it is a key for true happiness and contentment. What is it that you're thinking of doing?"

As the line crept forward, Hannah described the ideas she had for the nonprofit. Joan listened thoughtfully, nodding once or twice, a smile on her face.

"That really does sound like it's getting back to the basics, in the most literal of ways," she said. "A lot of people dealing with something like a traumatic brain injury find themselves having to start over, wouldn't you say?"

Hannah nodded. "Absolutely."

"And something like that sounds like it will be able to help so many people—not just the ones who suffered the injury but also their family members and then ultimately the people you employ. The actions of what you do—what anyone does—have far-reaching effects. That is something I always try to keep in mind when I am starting a business. I make sure my business concept is in line with my beliefs so I don't have to compromise my principles. It's important to get up everyday with a smile on my face, know that I've done the best job that I can do, and helped as many people as I encountered in a day, even if that means just making someone smile. For me, feeling happy comes from going back to the basics: being kind, caring about people, taking whatever your family unit is and making that important and making a list of priorities, which is different for everybody. However, whatever those priorities are, you need to be true to yourself. If that goes against what other people might want, stay strong in your belief and forge your own pathway."

Hannah watched the line move; the judge had reached the front of the line and was removing his shoes. "I hope you're right, Joan, about creating your own pathways. There is a part of me that feels I should just stay where I am, I'm already on this pathway so I might as well just stay there. I feel like I've made so many mistakes. I've done so many things for what I thought were the right reasons but they turned out not to be. I just didn't know. I started working in publishing because I love books. In addition, I suppose you could look at it and say that's meaningful work, that as an agent, you're helping get good writing out there to the public, but I've always felt like there was something more. That I was missing something, and for a while, I just assumed it was success, or money, or just being more established in my career. Nevertheless, the further I got in it, the more intense the feeling got that I wasn't doing the right thing. Then this really amazing manuscript came across my desk, and when I read it, I had this moment of *aha!*, like, this is that thing that's going to bring about that feeling for me, this is why I'm doing this. Then it didn't sell and there's a good chance the manuscript will never see the light of day. Moreover, people in publishing, they'll say, *Oh, that's just how it goes.*

You know, you win some, you lose some, but really, it was a wake up call."

"And that's what brought you to where you are today. All those mistakes! Those experiences have made you who you are and given you the depth to want more. You're going to fail; you're going to do things you're not happy about. Conversely, you're going to do a lot of things that you *are* happy with. What's important is your recognition of each one, taking responsibility for your actions and taking the time to understand what you did that worked well and what did not. Learn from your actions, how your decisions affected other people and how you can improve and move forward. If you do not take the time to evaluate yourself, it will be difficult to grow emotionally and be happy with yourself. Just remember, every challenge is nothing more than an opportunity for something better.

"The other thing about going back to basics is that it helps rid people of a sense of entitlement. No one is above the rules, yet there are so many people out there—from all walks of life—that would like to think they're special and above everyone else. People need to learn that respect is earned through humility and hard work, and not just automatically assigned because you have a certain title."

They'd reached the front of the line. Hannah caught sight of the judge ushering his family toward one of the terminals. She bent to untie her shoes.

She and Joan sat next to each other on one of the benches after they collected their personal things from the conveyor belt and put their shoes back on. When they stood up, Joan smiled and patted her shoulder.

"I really enjoyed chatting with you," she said. "And I wish you the best of luck in your new endeavors."

"Back to the basics, right?" Hannah said.

"Exactly," Joan said. The two women smiled at each other and then picked up their carry-ons and headed to their gates.

Chapter 7

FINDING ALIGNMENT

Hannah sat down in one of the empty chairs and waited for them to start boarding the flight. She pulled a pen and a small legal pad from her purse. The other people waiting were looking at their smart phones or laptops or up at the flatscreen TV hanging from the wall, broadcasting CNN on mute. Hannah thought about Joan and couldn't help but wonder how many more conversations people might be having with each other if the technology was turned off, if everyone really did get back to the basics, even if just for that one moment while they were all waiting.

She wrote: *Back to the basics.*

Followed by: *Bring families together.*

She thought about what it would be like to have a family of her own, to be married and happy, the way Brad and Christine were. How nice it must be to be able to sit on a park bench, on a gray, sunless day, and be completely content and happy with what you were doing.

Conner had not believed her when she told him she was coming back for Thanksgiving. "You're cruel," he groaned when she told him.

"No, I'm serious," she said. "I just booked the tickets. My flight gets in at two in the afternoon on Saturday."

"Well then," he said after a moment of silence. "I guess I am going to have to do everything in my power to see that I am down there to meet you when you arrive."

She wrote: *Make your own pie. Move your feet.*

She chewed on the end of the pen. *Natural gifts.*

This was the sort of thing you'd want to tape up on your bathroom mirror and look at every morning, she thought. She read the list once, then read it again. Around her, people started gathering their belongings and making their way to the gate. A woman came over the loudspeaker and announced they were going to start pre-boarding.

Hannah pulled her ticket out from her purse and double-checked her seat assignment. She looked at her list once more, then closed the legal pad and got up to wait in line to board the plane.

She had a window seat, though she would've preferred the aisle. It always felt like such a nuisance to have to bother the two people in the row if she had to get up to use the bathroom or just wanted to stretch her legs. But she liked getting to look out the tiny rectangular window as the plane reached altitude, the way everything fell away and looked miniscule, like toys or trinkets. The plane broke through the thick cloud cover, revealing blue skies and a bright sun.

The sun is always shining, she thought. Somewhere, the sun is always shining. She made a note to write that one down, too, once the seat belt sign was turned off and she could retrieve her purse from underneath the seat in front of her. Conner would like that one. He'd always said she should be more optimistic.

When the fasten seat belt light went off, Hannah leaned down and grabbed her purse. She pulled out the legal pad, as well as the women's resource center brochure. She tried to imagine what a brochure for her own organization might look like as she jotted down some notes about what things she'd have to do to make this change in her life.

After writing for a few minutes, she put the pen down and leaned back as far as the seat would allow. The whole thing suddenly seemed incredibly overwhelming. She rubbed her eyes and let her gaze go to the window, where the clouds had dissipated and the land below was green and brown and dotted with tiny buildings and bisected with curving roads that from this distance looked like little more than threads.

Hannah looked back to her tray table and saw that the man next to her also had a legal pad out that he was writing on. A word he'd written and circled at the top caught her eye: *Persistence.*

He glanced up and she smiled. "Sorry, I wasn't watching you or anything ... That word you wrote there, it kind of caught my eye." She nodded at his legal pad and then gestured to her own. "I'm kind of working on some of my own stuff here. And feeling a little overwhelmed about it, actually."

The man returned her smile. "Well, persistence for me is the difference between success and failure. In all the business ventures I have pursued it is always that never-quit mentality that keeps me on track. It always seems that everyone around you does not see the same potential and vision to building a business or making an investment. Sure, there are always the people that support whatever you do, but there are always many more who dissuade you from your goal. This has been true of every business opportunity or investment I have pursued. Now, with that said, I definitely take a close look at all aspects of the business or investment. However, once I have decided to move forward, I do not look back, and I never quit. It has served me well, whether or not it becomes one of my successes or failures is second to the fact that I did everything in my power to have a success. So to come back to my note pad, the word persistence is certainly an important trait to have, especially if you're feeling overwhelmed. A never-quit state of mind is the real mental push that always pushes me forward. It is such a key player in hitting my targets and ultimately my final goals. If you don't mind sharing, what are you working on?"

Hannah told him a little bit about her ideas for starting the nonprofit.

"That's very interesting," the man said. "What's your name, by the way? I'm David Michal."

"Hannah Braun."

"Do you have any experience with nonprofits?"

"Not really. But I'd like to think that I'm a fast learner, and also, it's something that I feel strongly about."

"That certainly helps. But persistence ... persistence is key. You can't give up. I know that sounds cliché, but it's true. And if what you're doing isn't working, you've got to reach out to new people and be open to finding new ways. Do you have people that can help you?"

"This whole idea is still pretty new. I haven't really told that many people about it yet. But I think when the time comes, yes, I hope I'll be able to find people who want to help."

David nodded. "Good. When you've got a core group of people that you can really trust, they'll listen to what you have to say and you'll listen to what they have to say and you might realize that what you're hearing is something that you hadn't previously been able to see."

"I guess that's one of the things I feel a little overwhelmed about. I know the people are out there, but it's a matter of finding them. It's like, I've got this vision, but I'm not exactly sure where to start looking for the people to help me bring it to fruition. I want to make sure I find the right people. I feel like that's important."

"You're right—it absolutely is. It's crucial that you find alignment with the right people. I'm actually involved with a nonprofit that focuses on helping communities, and one of the best things that our company has done—and that I think all companies should strive to do—is create programs that are sustainable. I've learned a lot about nonprofits since I've been involved with this one, and the one thing I can say about this one in particular is that the generosity factor is there but so is the belief that they have to build sustainable programs in order to help people long-term."

"That makes a lot of sense," Hannah said. "That you wouldn't want to burn through all your resources right away, even if it was in the name of helping, because in the long run that wouldn't do anyone any good."

"Exactly. You're at the helm; you want to be a good steward. And if you find success, often that means you didn't just do everything yourself. People will help you, mentor you, along the way. It could be investors or people you reach out to in the community. People who have gone through what you're looking to do and have some experience in the area."

"Or it could be the guy you sat next to on a plane."

David smiled. "Or that. When you're running a nonprofit, or any business, really, you want to make sure that the programs are sustainable. You want to be able to expand out to the world. Reach out to people, ask for help, look at models that work. You've got to set your goals and then not quit."

"I guess there is a part of me that's afraid that people are going to think I'm being foolish. Like this is just some impulsive idea I've got and it's not going to work out."

"But if you believe in it, and you're persistent, it won't matter, will it? And I promise you, not everyone is going to think that. But that's why you've got to find alignment with the right people. It can be hard asking for help, admitting that what you're doing isn't working out. But for me, whenever I've asked someone for help, when I've shown them my problems and opened myself up like that, I've ended up reaching out to somebody who identifies with what I'm doing, who basically says, *You know, we're not in the same business, you're doing something different than I'm doing, but I like what you're doing.* Because when you reach out to people, you'll be able to find people that have a common passion and all of sudden, doors will start opening. And maybe they say, *Hey, I'd like to get involved in something like that.* How generous can your company be?"

Hannah doodled on the corner of her notepad as she considered the question. "I'd like it to help as many people as possible. People that kind of fall through the cracks. I mean, it's something that I've witnessed first hand. I guess that's part of the reason why I feel like I could do something to help. Because I've been on both sides of it."

"You need to have the mentality of never quitting, even when it looks like everything is falling apart. Because honestly, Hannah? Every deal that I've ever done, at some point, looked like it was completely falling apart. So never quit, reach out as quickly as you can to people that have successfully accomplished what you're trying to do, and find alignment with it. And don't forget the generosity factor. Because the generosity factor, to me, in the eyes of the world, will propel your company even further."

She looked down at her notepad. Underneath what she'd already written she added: *Find alignment* and *Build sustainable programs.*

"That is really great advice," she said. "Thank you."

He smiled. "You're welcome."

Chapter 8

FAITH INSTEAD OF FEAR

A subtle anxiety started to swirl in Hannah's stomach; she first noticed it as the plane touched down at SFO and she simply attributed it to the slightly bumpy landing. But once her feet were on solid ground, propelling her toward the baggage claim where she planned to meet Conner, she realized the anxiety had strengthened and that it wasn't the landing she was nervous about. She was nervous about seeing Conner again.

She stopped mid-stride, right in front of a store selling designer handbags. She squinted. When did they start selling Coach and Louis Vuitton at the airport? The saleswoman eyed her like she couldn't decide if she should encourage Hannah to come into the store or ignore her in the hopes that she'd go away.

Hannah turned away and went over to one of the coffee shops. She debated ordering tea but then just decided to get the coffee. She dumped in half-and-half until the liquid was the color of caramel and sat down at an empty corner table.

The flight had actually arrived ahead of time, so it was a good possibility that Conner wasn't even there yet. Although, Hannah figured, he'd probably driven down with his mom, and his mom was someone who always got to places on time. When Hannah had first arrived on the east coast, she kept thinking how well Mrs. Tero would've fit in there.

She pried the lid off her coffee cup and blew at the steam. She watched as people hurried by, dragging luggage or small children, or, in a few cases, both. A man in a business suit rushed by, so involved with his phone conversation that he nearly plowed into one of the women trying to navigate a luggage cart with a toddler and then an infant strapped to her chest in a carrier.

Hannah took a few sips of her coffee and then finally forced herself up. She knew that Conner would be thrilled to see her, and any anxiety she was feeling was entirely her own. But what was it that she was nervous about? Actually seeing him in person? She slung her purse over her shoulder and gripped the suitcase handle. No, she realized, as she walked. It wasn't seeing Conner; it was telling him about her plans. Of everyone in her life, he'd been the happiest, the most proud, when she first got her internship, when she signed her first client, when one of her authors made *The New York Times* bestseller list. Would he think she was foolish for giving all that up?

She saw him as she came down the escalator. His back was to her but she'd recognize him anywhere. His dark hair was a little longer than she remembered it but that one little piece in the back was sticking up, like always. He turned, and for a moment still didn't see her. His mother stood next to him, also scanning the crowd. She looked toward the escalator and saw Hannah first, but she made no move to direct Conner's attention in that direction. She'd let him spot Hannah on his own, and when he did, a huge grin broke out on his handsome face.

He walked over, still with a slight limp from the many knee surgeries he'd undergone following his accident. He had an artificial kneecap, in fact. That was one of the first jokes Hannah remembered him making during his physical therapy—he was the Bionic Man now.

"Look at you," he said, wrapping her up in a hug. He lifted her off her feet. "I'm so happy to see you," he whispered.

"You too, babe." She kissed his cheek and then, when he released her, she hugged his mom, who had just as big a smile on her face.

"Hannah, you look wonderful," she said. "How was the flight? Come on; I'm sure you're ready to get out of here."

When they got to the car, Conner insisted that Hannah sit in the front seat, even though he'd undoubtedly be cramped sitting in the back.

"So tell me, dear," Mrs. Tero said. "How is life in New York? What big news do you have to report?"

Hannah looked out the window as they sped past the vacant parking lots that housed the Alemany flea market. She and Conner used to go there often during high school and had found all sorts of treasures, spending lazy afternoons browsing the various tables then going to their favorite taqueria for enchiladas.

"Remember that knight's armor we found at the flea market that one time?" Conner said, as though reading her mind. He laughed softly. "Too bad I wasn't wearing that the night of the accident."

It still unnerved her, the way he'd make jokes about the accident, or the way in which he'd speak about it, like he'd gotten a paper cut or stubbed his toe. It was his way of coping, Mrs. Tero had told her on more than one occasion, which Hannah tried to be understanding of but still found herself feeling sick to her stomach whenever Conner made a joke.

"I actually do have some news to report," Hannah said. She hadn't given much thought as to how she was actually going to tell people—or *what* exactly she was going to tell people—but she had a growing suspicion that the more she thought about how she was going to say it, the harder it would be. She fiddled with the clasp on her purse. "I've decided to change careers."

From behind her she heard a click as Conner undid his seatbelt. He slid to the middle seat and then leaned forward between the seats. "What do you mean?" he asked, looking at her intently.

Mrs. Tero cast her a sidelong glance. "Did something happen?"

Hannah shrugged. "Yes. No. I don't know. I always thought that this was what I wanted to be doing, but some things have happened as of late that have kind of made me realize it's not."

Conner touched her arm. "Are you okay?"

"Yes." She tried to give him a reassuring smile. "It's a good thing, actually. I know it sounds like I don't know what I'm talking about, but that's because it's a recent development. But I just realized I want to be doing something that is personally meaningful, that helps other people."

"So do you have something in mind?" Mrs. Tero asked.

"Yes, actually, I do. And I ... I guess I wanted to talk to you guys about it, because I think you'd be able to give me some good advice. I'd like to start a nonprofit that helps people with traumatic brain injuries lead independent lives." She looked at Conner, who was still leaning forward, his eyes on her. "You know, because it seems like once you're out of the hospital, once you're done with the physical therapy ... that's when some of the real challenges come up. Mainly because you're so focused on just getting home, on getting better, but once you're there ... then what?"

"I think that sounds like a really great idea," Mrs. Tero said. "And it's certainly something we would have utilized if one existed within a five-hundred-mile radius. And I'd be happy to sit down and talk with you about any questions you have."

"Thanks, Mrs. Tero. I was hoping to be able to talk to you about the kinds of things that would've helped you out the most. And you, too," she said to Conner.

"Oh, I could tell you plenty," he said coolly. He slid back to his seat and she heard the click of the seatbelt. Hannah swiveled around in her seat but Conner only stared out the window, a somber expression on his face.

"It's still a very new idea," Hannah said. "And I get that it might sound kind of crazy to just decide to do this, but it feels like the right decision. In a way, the whole thing is pretty scary, but what's more scary is feeling this way and not doing something about it."

"Well, good for you," Mrs. Tero said. "Hey, you know, I'm getting together with a friend tomorrow for lunch; why don't you join us? He's a great person to talk to and I think he might be able to give you some good advice. We're going to this new little brasserie in Sonoma. I think you'll like it."

"Okay," Hannah said. "That sounds great."

She looked out the window and saw the Golden Gate Bridge. Once they crossed that, it'd be another forty-five minutes north on the 101, and then they'd be home. Conner didn't say a word to her for the rest of the ride.

Hannah's parents lived at the foot of a small mountain where the view out the living room window was a vineyard. She sat there now, on the couch next to her mother, her father seated across from them in his recliner. Both her parents were looking at her with quizzical expressions, as though they couldn't quite believe what she'd just told them.

"But I thought your job was going really well," her mother finally said. "I thought you were really liking it."

Hannah shrugged and took a sip of her ice water, even though she wasn't thirsty. "My job is fine," she said.

"So why are you leaving then?" her father asked. He took his wire-rimmed glasses off and carefully cleaned the lenses with the hem of his shirt before replacing them on his face, as though somehow removing the smears might help him better understand what she was telling them.

"I just don't think I'm doing what I should be," she said.

Her mother pursed her lips. "Is that why you came all the way out here? To tell us that you're quitting your job?"

"No, Mom. I came out here because I wanted to see you guys."

"Did something happen?"

"If you're asking if something bad happened—no. Nothing like that at all. I just feel like there are other things I could be doing that would give my life more meaning."

Her father steepled his fingers and squinted at her. "Could you elaborate?" he said. "Could you explain to your mother and me why you're suddenly leaving your dream job? That you happen to be doing very well at, I might add."

Hannah licked her lips and tried not to feel like she was in the middle of a job interview that was going terribly wrong. "I've been thinking about this for a little while now. I want to do something that's going to help people. Something that, at the end of the day, I can feel good about."

"But do you know anything about starting a nonprofit? I'm not trying to sound unsupportive, but it just seems a little premature to me for you to jump ship when you've got a good job that you've worked really hard for." Her mother smiled. "Doesn't that count for something?"

"Yes, of course it does!" Hannah leaned over and placed her glass on one of the coasters on the coffee table in front of her. She rubbed her eyes and felt the beginnings of a headache, lurking on the horizon.

"Sweetpea, we just don't want to see you throw everything away on a whim," her father said. "We certainly know that you're smart and talented and are good at many things. We've always said that. But you've got to understand where we're coming from. We only want the best for you. You might be an adult, but we're still your parents, and we want to make sure that you're making the right choices."

"And I appreciate that. I thought you guys might be a little more excited."

"It's just so sudden!" her mother exclaimed. "Have you told anyone else about this? What made you decide to do this in the first place? It's quite a change. It's not like you're going from being a second grade teacher to a sixth grade teacher. This is a big change. It's very different. Your father and I don't want to see you do something on impulse that you might end up regretting later. It's like Dad just said: You're an adult now. You've got responsibilities you have to see to, and especially living somewhere like New York, I would hate to see you give up a good paying job for something that isn't so financially secure."

Hannah pressed on her temples and then stood up. "I'm going to go lie down for a little bit," she said. "I was up really early this morning and didn't get to sleep on the plane. We can talk more about this later, okay?"

She forced a smile and tried to ignore the troubled look on her parents' faces.

"Would you like me to make you a sandwich?"

"No thanks, Mom."

"Okay," her mom said. "Don't forget to call your sister. I promised her I'd tell you to call."

Hannah took her purse and suitcase and walked down the hallway to the staircase. She'd spent her whole childhood in this house, and sometimes it felt like she'd never left. The hallway walls were adorned with framed photographs chronicling her and her sister's lives from babyhood to present.

Upstairs, she walked past the bathroom to the end of the hallway to her room. She set her suitcase down and stood on the braided rug in the middle of the room and looked at her old desk where she used to sit and do homework, at the bookshelf lined with novels she'd read throughout high school. Her mother had been saying for years now that she planned to make Hannah's room over as her arts and crafts space, but it still hadn't happened and Hannah was beginning to suspect it never would.

She went over to her bed and sat down. She pulled the legal pad out of her purse and lay on her stomach, a blank page open in front of her. To keep herself from overanalyzing Conner's indifferent response to what she was planning to do, and her parents' doubts, she started to write down some of the things she'd like her nonprofit to do. She envisioned renting out a moderate-sized space, somewhere with good lighting that was easy to get to via public transportation. She could see a large main room, with comfortable chairs and the type of décor that would make people feel at ease, maybe wall-to-wall bookshelves. And there could be a few smaller offices, perhaps they could offer counseling services, or maybe even classes. She realized, as she stared at her list, that she wanted to talk to someone who might actually think this was a good idea, or someone who at least wouldn't tell her she was making a huge mistake. She picked up the old cordless phone that she'd spent countless hours talking on during middle- and high school and called her sister.

Kate listened while Hannah relayed both their parents' reactions and Conner's. Then she said, "Hmm," like she always did when she was trying to think of a certain way to put something.

"Well, Hannah," she finally said. "If it's something that you feel strongly about, I say go for it. I wouldn't worry too much about what Mom and Dad have to say. They weren't always thrilled with the choices I made, either." She laughed. "But that didn't stop me."

Hannah smiled. "True," she said. Her sister had married young, after a whirlwind romance with Mathias, a guy from Norway who was backpacking around the United States. Kate then decided to drop out of college so she and Mathias could open a restaurant. Hannah must've heard her mother repeat the phrase *Most new restaurants fail within the first year of opening* dozens of times, but Kate and Mathias's restaurant, Oasis, which offered an eclectic world-fusion menu, seemed to do better and better each year. And somehow, Kate found the time to care for her two young children as well.

"Are you coming down here for Thanksgiving? Or are you going to stay up there?" Kate asked.

"I think I'll come down there. If that's okay."

"Absolutely. And weren't you asking me about the Turkey Trot? I am doing that this year, if you want to come with. Plenty of people will be walking, if that makes it any more enticing."

"Well, I forgot to pack my running shoes, so I guess I will have to walk it, but yes, I'd like to go. So I'll probably be down there on Wednesday, then. I'll let you know, though."

"Sounds great. I've gotta get going; I've got to pick up Anna from her riding lesson. She's excited to see you. Don't let Mom and Dad discourage you too much, okay? I think you've got a great idea. It really could be something."

"Thanks, Kate. I'll see you in a few days." Hannah hung up the phone and lay back on her bed, staring up at the ceiling, where the glow-in-the-dark stars she had stuck up there two decades ago still were, waiting for night to fall so they could shine.

The next afternoon, Hannah met Mrs. Tero and Mrs. Tero's friend, Yvan Gosselin, for lunch. Yvan smiled at her when he shook her hand and said, "Vivian tells me you're thinking of changing careers."

"Tell him what it is you're thinking of doing," Mrs. Tero said. "It's really such a great idea."

Hannah described the vision she had, which was slowly becoming more clear. "I was writing down some ideas yesterday, kind of brainstorming, and one of the great things about this is that it can be really flexible. So what we offer can kind of change based on the needs of the … clients, I guess is what you'd call them. I'd like to see as many services as possible be free or very low cost. My first roommate when I moved to New York was a grant writer, and she said there's actually a lot of money available for these sorts of things—you just have to know where to look. Clearly, I still have a lot of stuff to figure out. But … that's what I'm thinking."

She looked down at her menu. "I told my parents yesterday. They weren't too thrilled. Conner didn't seem that excited about it, either. I thought he would be."

Mrs. Tero reached across the table and patted her hand. "Maybe you should talk to him about that."

"Did he say something to you?"

"No, but I'm sure he wouldn't mind having some alone time with you to just talk about things. I think he's been feeling a little restless lately."

"Okay," Hannah said.

Yvan rested his forearms on the table and smiled at her. "Hannah, I love that idea."

"You do?"

"I do. Because the thing I believe more than anything else is the ability to inspire others to become better and to feel better in all circumstances. And that sounds exactly like what you're going to try to do."

"It's nice to talk to people who think it's actually a good idea."

"And don't be discouraged if you run into challenges along the way; it's almost a guarantee that you will. The unfortunate reality is that the majority of people maintain thoughts which drain them, rather than bring them to achieve greater development. You should always be striving to maintain positive value-added thoughts and hope, even in the darkest moments. And everyone goes through them. At the same time, it's not always about having exclusively positive thoughts. You don't have to be happy *all* the time. If you take the time to define a clear goal, it will give you something to focus on even when things aren't going exactly how you hoped they might."

"I guess what I'm struggling with right now," Hannah said, "is translating my ideas into actions. I mean, I'm pretty clear about my goals, but sometimes it seems so overwhelming to actually manifest them."

"You've got to be tenacious. Never give up. It's so easy—and tempting!—to let ourselves wander without knowing which direction to take. If you've got tenacity, self-confidence, the strategic ability to control barriers, and the development of strength from failures, it is possible to come back from anything. If you've got the necessary drive and motivation, you can reach new levels and achieve great success. I might sound like a broken record, but you've got to remember to never give up. And to have faith instead of fear. Work with a renewed idea of better days. I like to repeat the famous phrase by the great French pharmacist Emile Coue: *Day by day, in all areas of my life, I am getting better and better.*"

Mrs. Tero smiled. "That's one of my favorite quotes."

"I've heard that saying before," Hannah said. "I never knew who said it. It's a good one."

"It is."

"But what about on the days when you don't feel like you're getting better? What do you do when it feels like everything you're doing isn't making a difference at all, or it's making things worse?"

"I'm going to tell you the formula I follow. It's helped me immeasurably over the years. First, take a step back and get the big picture of whatever is happening. Your interpretation of facts is often exaggerated compared to the reality. Then, instead of focusing on the dark side of the situation, look on the bright side and try to keep it alive in your spirit, even if things seems desperate. In reality, there is no despair in life. Consider alternatives and set new goals, and allow yourself to feel a longing desire to reach these objectives. Then crystallize this desire into a clearly defined purpose. Finally, act appropriately to achieve these new goals."

Hannah took a sip of water and set her glass down. "I feel like I should be writing this down."

"One last thing, Hannah," Yvan said. "Remember that your attitude toward life is more important than your abilities."

A slow smile spread across Hannah's face as an image of Conner came into her mind. "I know someone who lives that every day."

Chapter 9

STAY POSITIVE

After lunch, Mrs. Tero and Yvan invited Hannah to walk around Sonoma Square with them.

"Actually, I think I'm going to stop by your house and see what Conner's up to," Hannah said. "And then I promised my mom I'd get her car back before dinner time, so I'm sure I'll see you in the next few days."

"Sounds good, Hannah," Mrs. Tero said.

Yvan shook her hand again and gave her a big smile. "Keep me posted," he said. "I'm curious to hear how this all works out for you. You'll be great—just remember that."

"Thanks, Yvan. It was great to meet you. I'm glad we had the chance to talk."

She got back on Highway 12 and started to drive to the Tero's. It was a mild day, so she rolled her window down and let the breeze blow her hair around. She missed driving, she realized. She zoomed past acres and acres of grape vines, their leaves brown and dry and fluttering to the ground. She took a deep breath.

When she got to the Tero's, she found Conner in the driveway, shooting hoops.

"You're pretty good," she said as she got out of the car. He took a shot and the ball sailed through the net.

"Thanks," he said. "Who knew I had a hidden basketball talent."

"You busy?"

He retrieved the ball from the edge of the lawn. "How was lunch?"

"Good. Your mom's friend Yvan is pretty cool."

"Yeah, he is."

"I've got a few hours until I've got to get the car back to my mom. Want to hang out?"

And finally, he smiled. "Of course. But let's get out of here, yeah? Let's go somewhere."

"Where do you want to go?"

"I've actually got a friend of my own I'd like you to meet."

"Okay," Hannah said. "That sounds great. Let's go."

Conner's friend was a young man named Camden Garcia, who was on the teen advisory council at the hospital Conner's mom worked at. He waved as they pulled up and walked out of the garage toward them.

"Camden," Conner said as they got out of the car. "How's it going? I wanted you to meet my friend Hannah."

"Hey, nice to meet you," Camden said. He and Hannah shook hands.

"You too," Hannah said. She looked over his shoulder into the garage. "What are you working on in there?"

"Want to see?"

"Sure."

They walked into the garage and Camden showed them his work area, where he was making metal crosses. "I started making these crosses to give away at church. I give one every Sunday."

"Wow," Hannah said, picking one of the finished crosses up. "That's really cool."

"We sell some at coffee shops, too, and local fundraisers. We actually do a lot of fundraising with them. Would you like one?"

"Oh … I … well, sure," Hannah said. "Thank you."

Camden smiled. "You're welcome."

"How long have you been making these for? They're really, very good."

"It's something I started doing a little while ago. I had a brain tumor and had to have surgery and in that time I really turned to God. And I started making these crosses to give away."

"Wow," Hannah said, looking down at the cross in her hand.

"Camden is the man to talk to if you need a little positivity in your life," Conner said. "He's certainly helped me a lot."

"Well, you can't get stuck on the here and now," Camden said. "Focus on the positive things in life. Don't let a closed door stop you. Push through it, no matter how many closed doors come your way."

"I've got a couple doors I'm trying to get through right now, actually," Hannah said.

"You can do it. You've just got to stay positive. And it's important to have goals. Short-term and long-term ones. In my situation, the Make-A-Wish Foundation gave me something to look forward to. I got to go to Texas Motor Speedway to meet Jeff Gordon and we had such a great time. We got to ride in a limo, stay in a hotel, all that fun stuff. And then long-term goals are also important."

Hannah smiled. "A co-worker actually took me to hear Frank Shankwitz speak recently. He was really inspiring. That's so awesome your family was able to do that."

"It really was such a blessing for me and my family. It was something to look forward to. And focusing on the good things that have happened really helped me, and would really help anyone, in any situation. You've just got to stay positive. You've got to try to find the positive in all situations. Whatever has to be done has to be done, and you just have to get through each day."

"That is really great advice," Hannah said. "What would be even better is if I could actually put it into practice."

"You can," Camden said. "But that's just it: you have to practice at it."

"I'm going to try to," Hannah said. "I really am."

She drove west and got onto the 1, which was her absolute favorite road to drive on. She looked to her left at the Pacific Ocean, which always seemed so much bigger than the Atlantic.

"So," she said to Conner. "I wanted to talk to you. I get the distinct feeling that you're not thrilled with what I'm doing. I thought of everyone, you'd be the most excited."

"It's not that, Han," he said. He rubbed the lower part of his face. "I don't even really know exactly what your new plan is, and yeah, what you've told us sounds interesting. But … I guess I just wonder why you're doing it. It seems like a big change."

"Weren't you always the one telling me change is good?"

"Yes. Aren't you happy, though? Being an agent?"

"I thought I was."

"And you're good at it."

"I guess."

"No, you are."

"I want to do something that helps other people, though."

"Don't get me wrong, Han. It's a good idea. And there's nothing wrong with wanting to help other people. But are you just doing this because you feel guilty? Because you're trying to prove something?"

"What?" She turned her head and looked at him. "Prove something?"

"I didn't mean it like that."

"How did you mean it, then?"

"I mean that I think you feel guilty about the way things went down and that this is your way of trying to get rid of that."

Hannah frowned. She turned her blinker on and yanked the car over to the side of the road.

"So you think I should just keep doing something that I don't really love? That I don't feel passionate about?"

"No. I think you should absolutely do something you feel strongly about."

"Then why are we having this conversation? You resent me, don't you. You resent me for leaving you. I knew you did. And you know what? I don't blame you. I'd resent me, too. You are totally justified in resenting me." She burst into tears.

"I'm not mad at you," Conner said. "God, you think I resent you? You think I'm mad at you? I never was. You know that, right, Hannah? I would've been mad at you if you'd stayed."

Hannah wiped at her eyes. Conner looked at her. "Don't cry, babe," he said. "There is no doubt in my mind that you did the right thing. What were you supposed to do? Stay somewhere that you'd been waiting forever to get away from? You would've been miserable."

"But what about you? You wanted to get away from here, too."

"Yeah, but not like you. I mean, part of me wanted to go just because it was something that you wanted. I'm okay with small-town life." He laughed. "Which is good because that's exactly what I've got." Her chin trembled and he took her face between his hands. "Listen to me," he said. "The only thing that upsets me is thinking that you're out there feeling guilty about this. Things happen. That's life."

"It was my fault, though."

"Hannah, it wasn't."

"Yes, it was."

She'd replayed the scenario in her mind countless times. She was supposed to meet Conner at the skate park and just hadn't felt like leaving the house. What had been the reason? That part she could no longer recall. But she knew it hadn't been something legitimate: she hadn't been sick, hadn't been in the middle of a big homework assignment. She just didn't want to go, for whatever reason, and when he called her to see when she'd be arriving she'd told him she wasn't coming.

"Okay," he'd said agreeably, and she could still hear his voice as though he'd just whispered the sentence to her now, "I'll come to you."

Now, she looked at him, really looked into those blue eyes that were so familiar, yet since the accident, also very different, and she tried to detect even the slightest shred of dishonesty, but she couldn't. He meant it. Everything he said he meant, and that's the way it always had been with him, that was one of the things she loved about him.

"I just think how things might've been different if I'd met you at the skate park like we planned. You don't ever think about that?"

"No."

"But why?"

"Because what's the point? It's like choosing to never leave your house again because you might get hit by a bus when you try to cross the street. Except by staying at home all the time you end up falling down the stairs or choking on your breakfast. The purpose of life is to live. Really live. And that's what you're doing. And I'm so proud of you for that."

She took a deep breath and leaned her head against his shoulder. He put his arm around her and said, "That's why I'm surprised when you tell me you want to just stop what you're doing. I'm not saying you shouldn't, but I don't want you to completely upend your life because you think you owe me. Or because you feel guilty."

"But that's not why I want to do it. I want to do it because I feel like I'm not really living life doing what I'm doing now. Like, maybe on the outside it looks like I've got it pretty good—and I'm thankful for all the opportunities and lucky breaks I've caught along the way—but at the end of the day I don't feel like I've really contributed anything. I don't feel like what I'm doing is really meaningful. And if it is, it's only in the most superficial of ways."

"Hey, books are meaningful."

"I know, but ... it's different. I mean, if you had the opportunity to go to a place that could help you live independently, that could provide you with resources that could point you in that direction ... wouldn't you want to do that?"

"That does sound pretty awesome. You know what I would really love to do, though? I'd love to get out of here. Just for a few days. I'd love to go somewhere, without my mom feeling like she has to tag along. I'm thirty-one years old! I don't always need my mother to be my chauffeur. Or do I?" He chuckled and shook his head. "It'd be nice, that's for sure."

Hannah lifted her head. She brushed down his lock of hair that always defiantly stood up. "Let's do it, then," she said. "Let's get out of here."

"Really?"

"Really. Let's go rent a car and get out of here. We can drive down to my sister's for Thanksgiving. She'd love to see you."

His eyes widened. "Don't tease me, Hannah."

"I'm not. I was just thinking how much I missed driving, and I would love to just take the next few days and drive down the 1. There's this road race I want to go to on Thanksgiving Day, actually."

"Road race? Since when do you run?"

"I don't, but Kate's doing it. It's for charity. It'd be cool to check out."

Conner leaned over and kissed her forehead. "You always know exactly what I need."

Chapter 10

TO GO BEYOND

They rented a car in Santa Rosa and left early the next morning. Conner sat in the passenger seat, a map unfolded on his lap.

"Yep," he said, laughing, folding the map after a minute. "Still no good at reading maps."

"I figured we'd just stay on the 1. We can take our time. Stay in a hotel or something. Make it actually feel like a vacation instead of just coming home to see family. Not that that isn't important." She grinned. "I had to promise my mom I'd spend a day in the city with her when we got back. She's glad we're doing this though; she's always after me to go visit Kate."

"And," he said, "this will give you plenty of time to really tell me about this organization you want to start."

"Okay," Hannah said. "I would love to."

They decided to stop on the Central Coast, in San Luis Obispo. "My mom told me she read somewhere that this is supposedly the happiest place on Earth," Conner said.

Hannah shut the car door and stretched, feeling something crack pleasantly in her back. "I believe it," she said. "This place is beautiful. Are you hungry? Let's get something to eat."

They walked down the narrow sidewalk, past rows of nineteenth-century buildings. "This place looks good," Conner said as they passed the door of a café called Innovate.

"Sure," Hannah said. "Let's check it out."

She was surprised, though, when they entered the restaurant, to see that instead of separate tables, the dining area was comprised of five long wooden tables with benches on either side. She glanced at Conner.

"Are you—" she started to say but stopped when the hostess appeared in front of them.

"Welcome to Innovate!" the hostess said. "Is this your first time visiting us?"

"Yes," Conner said.

"Well, one of the things we pride ourselves on is being a community dining experience. I'm here to give you menus, but you may seat yourselves. As you can see, we encourage our patrons to share their dining experience with others."

"Great," Conner said. Hannah tried to look a little less skeptical.

They took their menus and sat down on one of the benches. Hannah couldn't help but feel a little awkward, as though she were the last one to arrive to a party. Conner, though, seemed completely at ease as he struck up a conversation with the guy directly across from him.

Hannah looked down at the menu and tried not to be annoyed with the whole thing. What if she didn't feel like conversing with the other restaurant patrons? What if she had something she wanted to tell Conner and didn't want to announce it to the whole table? She knew they could've just as easily picked a different restaurant, and that she was probably feeling irritated because she was hungry, but she still couldn't help but feel annoyed at the place. She put the menu down. Conner was still talking to the man, the two of them conversing as though they were good friends who had't seen each other in a while. Hannah looked to her right. The person seated closest to her was a woman who didn't appear much older than she was, with long blond hair and wide blue eyes. The woman saw Hannah looking and offered her a smile.

"Is this your first time here?" she asked.

Hannah nodded. "Yes," she said. "How did you know?"

"You look a little bewildered. Sometimes it throws people off at first, the whole idea of sitting next to complete strangers while you're eating your meal."

"It is a little surprising. Or unexpected, I guess."

"It's great, though, because you can have some really interesting conversations. And meet some great people. What's your name?"

"Hannah."

"I'm Stacee Nelson."

"Nice to meet you. My friend and I are kind of on an impromptu road trip."

Stacee smiled. "That sounds like fun."

"It's has been, so far. I've been living in New York for the past decade and I guess I didn't realize how much I miss driving."

"What do you do in New York?"

"I'm a literary agent."

"Oh, that must be exciting."

"Well, I *was* a literary agent. I'm going to be changing careers. I want to start a nonprofit."

"Good for you! It can be a little scary at first, huh?"

Hannah nodded. "Yes. But I feel like it's something I have to do. Even if they are two totally different things and some people think I'm crazy for doing so."

Stacee took a sip of her drink and set it down. "You should try the iced tea—it's great. I was in corporate finance for many years but have recently transitioned to becoming a full-time entrepreneur. And actually, if you want to go even further back, in my twenties, I was a social worker."

"Wow," Hannah said. "You've done a lot of different things. I think that's cool, though. You tried different things out until you found what you were really passionate about, right?"

"Exactly. It can be difficult to make that change, however, especially if you're leaving something you've been doing for a while or you've got people who think you should stay right where you are. It really takes courage. Courage is such an important trait. The courage to go beyond your comfort zone, to dream bigger, to attempt more, to achieve more"

"My parents think I'm making a big mistake. They're probably the least enthused about my plans."

"It can be really hard when the people closest to you aren't supportive of what you want to do. The support of friends and family is important, but don't let their own fears and uncertainties hold you back from achieving your goals and fulfilling your purpose. It might be a difficult road sometimes, and uncomfortable to move away from the unconditional support of others, but if you have faith in yourself, unflinching integrity in your actions, and the courage to take that step anyway, you'll be able to tackle anything."

Hannah thought back to one of her last conversations with Conner before she moved to New York. "I should stay here with you," she told him. He'd only stared at her with those dark blue eyes that still struck her as hypnotic and endless. "Hannah, are you crazy? You can't stay here. You've got to go. You've got to get out of here. It's what you want. And you're going to do it. You're going to step out of your comfort zone and do this." Now, she was aware of him sitting next to her on that wooden bench, chatting happily with some guy he'd just met, and she could feel his happiness, his pleasure at being somewhere new, having a conversation with someone he didn't know.

Their waitress came over and Hannah quickly scanned the menu again and decided on the steak salad and an iced tea.

"You want to split a milkshake with me?" Conner asked after he ordered a burger.

"Sure," Hannah said.

"One chocolate milkshake, two straws," he told the waitress with a grin.

Hannah looked back at Stacee. "I have a question," she said. "Or, rather, I'd like to know your thoughts on this. Especially since you've changed careers before. While I don't totally agree with my parents, I can understand why they're saying the things they are. I get where they're coming from. So I guess that just kind of brings up doubt and uncertainty, which makes it hard not to wonder if maybe they've got a point."

"Well, there's certainly nothing wrong with taking into account what their concerns might be. In fact, the guidance and advice of important people in your life may help you clarify your intentions and purpose. But yes, if it's something you feel strongly about, if you feel it's the right direction for you … then you have to be willing to move forward despite their concerns. Having faith is so important. It doesn't have to be God, either—though it certainly could be. But believing in yourself, *knowing* yourself, your value, your morals, your ethics, what you want ... This will help you move forward with courage and integrity."

Hannah nodded. "I like what you said about unflinching integrity. I don't know if I've achieved that yet, but that's something I'd like to get to someday."

"It's an ideal to strive for, part of being the best version of you, of who you want to be. Sometimes you fall short of it. It happens to everyone. The best thing you can do is not give up.

"And surround yourself with like-minded people who inspire and encourage you," she added. "It's so empowering and so beautiful. You'll really be amazed at what you can do."

"I want to believe that. And I guess there's this part of me that knows I'm heading in the right direction and I just need to make that leap. But at the same time, there's another part of me that thinks I should play it safe, and maybe my parents are right and I'm making a big mistake. Maybe I don't know what I'm doing. Maybe I can't do this."

"You can." Stacee nodded. "But this is one of those times when you've got to dig deep, have faith in yourself, and find the courage to just do it. For all of my education and world travels and business success, when I started down the path to becoming an entrepreneur, I felt like I didn't know anything. Until that point, I wasn't truly awake, wasn't living to my fullest potential. And in a period of a few months, my whole world opened up. I started associating with entrepreneurs and business owners from all walks of life. I aligned myself with mentors who could help me on my journey. And I was surrounded by new ideas, greater opportunities. It takes courage and faith to walk away from the comfort of a job and established career, to believe that you can branch out on your own for a bigger, better, brighter future.

"Maybe you want to consider changing the way you think about this new direction," Stacee went on: it's not so much that you're doing it for yourself but rather that you're doing it to help other people. That if you don't do it, many people will not benefit from the gift you were meant to give. So you're still essentially doing the same thing, but you've switched your mindset. It's like, if you're someone who's afraid of public speaking." She took a sip of tea. "Instead of focusing on you getting up there in front of a crowd and how afraid you are, switch the way you think about it. It's not about you; it's about your ultimate goal, which is bigger than you. In many cases, it's far-reaching and will affect many people."

"I do dislike public speaking," Hannah said. "But that's really good advice. And you know, if I presented it to my parents in that way, that it wasn't about me so much as being able to help other people ... I think they'd really be into that. I can't see them saying, *No, you're making the wrong choice; we don't want you to help other people.*"

Stacee smiled. "Exactly. Remember, not everyone is going to support your vision nor have the courage to pursue their own dreams; some may even want to hold you back. The best thing you can do when that happens is recognize that it's not about you, it's about their own fears and insecurities. It's not really about you."

"That's great advice—thank you."

"You're very welcome. I think you should be proud of yourself that you've decided to go this direction in your life. It really does take courage."

"It definitely helps to be able to talk to someone that's changed careers. I should tell my parents that, on my travels, I met someone who had changed careers a few times and was actually doing very well and was happy with the way things had worked out. Maybe that will give them a vote of confidence, if I can't."

The waitress came by with their food, then Hannah took a few bites and tasted the chocolate milkshake. She took a sip of the iced tea, which was as good as Stacee said it would be. She could practically feel her blood sugar levels starting to rise.

"This place is pretty cool, huh?" Conner said. "Man, if I lived in the area, I'd probably come here everyday." He gazed at Hannah. "You look like you're feeling better."

"I am. I think I just needed to get some food in me. And have a good conversation. This is Stacee, by the way," she said. "Stacee, this is my friend Conner."

Hannah ate some more and enjoyed the conversation with the people sitting nearby. Having a restaurant like this actually was a good idea, she realized. Would she have had this conversation with Stacee if she and Conner had been sitting in a booth, facing each other with no one on either side?

When Stacee and her friends were getting ready to leave, Hannah thanked her again for talking.

"Just remember to have courage, Hannah, and faith in yourself. You're going to do just fine," Stacee said.

"I'm going to work on it. I started this list of helpful ideas and phrases, and I'm definitely going to add that to it."

"Good. I hope you guys enjoy the rest of your road trip."

"We will. Actually, do you have a good hotel recommendation? We're probably going to stay over here tonight." Hannah smiled. "Maybe come back here for breakfast tomorrow before we hit the road."

Stacee thought for a moment. "There are a lot of great little places, but actually, this woman I know recently opened up a hotel not too far from here."

"Oh, really?" Hannah said. "That'd be great, actually. I figured we'd just find a place with a vacancy sign up. But yeah, we probably should consider where we're going to stay."

Stacee gave them directions to the hotel, which was about ten minutes from where they were.

"It was great to meet you guys," she said. "Good luck with everything."

Chapter 11

HARMONIC AMBIANCE

They had no trouble finding the hotel, which was adjacent to a vineyard and a winery. "It's like we never left the North Bay!" Conner said, with a grin on his face as he burst through the doors. And from the moment they walked in, they experienced an immediate and subtle shift … they glanced at each other in amazement and awe … wow … this feeling and sense of well-being came over them—being in this space felt different … inviting, soothing and healing … like they were being given a big, healthy and healing hug —it felt awesome! They instinctively took in a deep breath through their noses and smelled an invigorating citrus scent in the air, immediately noticing that they could breathe a bit deeper, their nasal passages opened up a bit more than before and they felt more energized. Mmmm … As they walked in a little further they started to notice this amazing, uplifting music playing—the actual sound was super clear with deep, bass tones—and the music, it was happiness-invoking! They started to bop up and down a little and Hannah could feel her mood further elevating as she moved to this very cool, sexy, contagious sound. Slightly mesmerized, they both continued to look around, and noticed the way people were interacting with each other—the way the staff was interacting with each other and the guests certainly stood out above and beyond what they had seen good customer service look like anywhere else. They could see that there was appreciation, compassion and respect between the people—the way that they addressed each other was so kind and respectful—it was almost palpable! How nice! They could feel themselves become even further uplifted by witnessing this. It was truly soothing, and in that moment, for the first time, Hannah truly got the sense of what "good vibes" in a place felt like. Conner felt a child-like warmth in his heart and felt like skipping! As he continued to move through the space … aware, appreciating, smelling, and moving to the sounds of the uplifting music, he started to notice some of the art on the walls. There were pictures of nature and of animals. As he examined one of them a little deeper, he found himself being transported to a different place and time and he heard himself saying, "Wow" outloud … as he was getting further inspired, his imagination was growing, his mind was expanding, ramping up his creativity—and right there he began to see possibilities for a project he had been thinking about. Where he had been stuck for months, clarity had now emerged! "This is incredible! Yes! That's it!" he thought to himself ... Woohoo!

Just as he was processing all of this, some movement out of the corner of his eye caught his attention and as he glanced to his left, a hotel host was approaching him—walking as though he was floating—so gracefully ... wearing a gleaming, kind smile and a beautiful, flowing mint-green uniform.

He was holding a tall, frosted, cool glass of water and said, "Good day sir. May I offer you some oxygenated purified alkaline water? Some of the benefits that you'll enjoy are: detoxification—so you can flush out deadly toxins, improved mental clarity—so you can have more mental focus, increased energy—so you can have an energy boost without the calories, improved digestion—so you can feel lighter and have more energy, improved appearance of your hair and skin—so you can feel sexier and younger and super hydration without bloating—so your skin and organs are nourished while you maintain a leaner look ... just to name a few haha. If you'd like to know even more about the benefits, you can read up about the water and other tools at our organic juice bar right over there or at our full-service organic restaurant around the corner. We also have an enlightened bookstore that has resources you may enjoy."

Wow, Conner thought ... this place was blowing his mind! "Yes, I would love to have some of that, thank you." And he took a large, refreshing gulp. He felt alive, refreshed and revitalized. "This is some great tasting water, it's delicious! I appreciate you sharing it! Thanks again."

"Yes it is delicious, isn't it? I'm glad you like it." The host smiled genuinely. Conner took another pause to look around, taking it all in ... and saw a large sparkling cathedral stone at the far end of the lobby.

The host noticed him looking at it and said, "Amethysts are positive energy stones that work on spirituality, your physical well-being and can also help with emotional issues. Isn't it a beautiful piece?"

"Yes, indeed it is—this whole place is just spectacular—it feels so ... wonderful and inviting being here," said Conner. "Yes, it is the effect of our harmonic ambiance," the host said. "There are many elements and components to it. Our founder Jote is the creator of the concept." The host pulled out an iPhone and said, "Would you like me to check you in, sir? I can do that right here from our app so you don't have to wait in line."

"Oh, actually we don't have a reservation," Conner said. "Hannah's friend gave us the tip to come here at the last minute. Hannah's the one right there heading over to the front desk now, but thank you and what a convenient feature; I've never seen that anywhere before ." As he glanced across the room, he saw the hotel lobby was spacious and eclectic, with mosaics and scattered lights across the ceiling that made him think of looking up at the sky on a perfectly clear night. He felt soothed and happy from the effects of this environment. He noticed that he was more present than he had been in years and he felt grateful.

Hannah was walking and bopping and exploring her way over to the front desk, taking it all in too ... she stopped as she noticed a podium with a menu of amenities the hotel provides and her eyes grew larger in excitement when she read it:

TRUISO Hotels Amenities include:
TRUISO Holistic Health Rooms—featuring:
alkaline water, organic towels, yoga for travelers, pilates for travelers, trampoline classes, and state of the art healthy cardio machines; salt-water pool; enlightened book store; and the Cozy Tantra Social Lounge, featuring organic spirits, organic wines, organic juices, a meditation garden, and more ...

This was all very exciting to Hannah and right up her alley. She was vibrating with excitement, looked down at the piece of paper Stacee had given her and headed over to the counter.

"Hi!" she said to the girl behind the counter. "We don't have reservations but we were hoping to book a room for tonight."

The girl smiled. "I'd be happy to help you with that," she said.

"Are you Jote by any chance? Also known as Rebecca J.P. Kaur?" Hannah asked.

"No I'm not, but did you need to talk to her? She's teaching a yoga class in our international board room for a group of world ambassadors. She teaches groups right in their meeting room; it's pretty cool. She's a great teacher, you should check out her class. She also has downloadable videos for travelers you can find on the TRUISO website if you don't catch her class. She will be here tomorrow morning at our organic community breakfast feast, from eight to eleven. You guys should come and then you'd have a chance to meet her there. She's very friendly."

"Wow that sounds intriguing and fantastic, we will definitely be there," Conner chimed in. "And we will be sure to bring our appetites—sounds delicious too."

"Great!" the girl said. "If you wouldn't mind filling out this form real quick so I can start getting you checked in. We are thrilled to have the two of you staying here with us at TRUISO hotel. You'll be staying in our Lapland room."

"Thank you. The what room?" Hannah asked as she started to write her information down on the appropriate lines.

"Lapland ... all of the rooms in this hotel represent a different place in the world. I think you'll find the Lapland room very inspiring."

"Hmm. Okay," Hannah said. "Though I must admit, I don't even know where that is."

"It's okay; I didn't know at first either," said the girl, giving her a conspiratorial smile. "It's a region in northern

Finland, and also parts of Sweden, Norway, and Russia. The room itself is very beautiful. It's one of my favorites here, actually."

"Well ... I can't wait to see it then." Hannah smiled.

Hannah finished filling out the paperwork and was given a key to their room, which was on the second floor. As they opened the door to their room, the door knob made no sound and then when the door closed behind them it was practically imperceptible.

The first thing they noticed was there was soft, pleasant lighting, a chic, futuristic-looking recycling bin by the desk, and a card with a list of amenities that read:

Each TRUISO hotel room features the following health-enhancing items:

Organic memory foam mattresses and ergonomic pillows
Organic linens
Sustainable coconut-palm flooring
Non-toxic paint
Organic aromatherapy
Alkaline water
Organic alkaline coffee and tea
Chlorine free shower-filters
Organic non-toxic soaps and creams
Organic towels
EMF protection devices
Sustainable eco-friendly furniture

And all rooms are cleaned with chemical-free products!

If you enjoyed using any of these health-supporting items and want to purchase any of them for yourself or a loved one, please visit us at our online store or ask to speak with one of our hosts at the hotel and we'll be happy to support you with your purchase. In addition, if you are interested in becoming an affiliate or distributor to earn additional income by referring any of these products, we can show you how to do that as well.

Thank you for your patronage, blessings to you and supporting you always on your journey in Chic Organic Health!

—TRUISO Corporation

They looked at each other and smiled in excitement and delight.

They looked around the room and took in the décor, which was mostly neutral with a splash of bright color thrown in here and there. They noticed a circular rug comprised of crimson and orange hues and an ice-blue armchair. Most interesting, though, to Hannah, were the photographs. She studied the large portrait of the Northern Lights that adorned one of the walls. Though she wasn't a huge fan of the extreme cold, after seeing this beauty she felt inspired to see the Northern Lights in person. Next to that photo was a landscape, showing a vast expanse of ice with a herd of reindeer in the distance, the sun setting behind them.

"This is beautiful," Conner said. "I can see the Ikea influence."

Hannah laughed. "I think it's the other way around." She looked back to the photograph with the reindeer. "Can you imagine what it'd be like to live somewhere where the sun didn't set for months?"

"That'd be pretty dope," Conner said. "What do they call it?"

"The midnight sun, I think. Supposedly you can play golf all night long."

Conner laughed and stretched out on the bed. "Sounds like my dad's version of paradise." He yawned. "Although I'm energized and kind of in awe from this place, I'm also ready to unwind," he said, patting the empty spot next to him. "Come sit."

Hannah sat down, the mattress giving in, in that particular way that memory foam does. "This mattress feels really great. They say it's organic, huh? "Yeah", Conner said, "Let's go on their website and learn more about it all later, OK? This place is super cool; I'm really intrigued. Hey and Hannah, thanks for letting me tagalong," he said. "I've kind of been needing something like this for … for a while now."

Hannah stretched out next to him, her back against his chest, and she pulled his arm around her waist.

"I agree, what a nice surprise coming here, and I'm glad we're getting to do this together, too," she said. "Kind of like old times."

Even though she wasn't facing him, she knew he was smiling. And they fell into a deep, restful sleep.

The next morning, Hannah stood by the window, running a comb through her wet hair, which she had just washed with the organic, non-toxic shampoo and conditioner—it felt and smelled great. She could hear the muffled sounds of Conner singing in the shower. She finished with her hair and set the comb down on a side table next to the couch, knocking over a wood photo frame. She straightened the frame and then noticed a glossy pamphlet next to it. The photograph on the front side of the pamphlet, of a man with a dark beard and bright blue eyes, was the same as the framed picture. He was standing next to a woman with a fair complexion and white-blond hair, and in front of them were two children. Hannah started to read the block of text below the picture.

This is Olavi, and his wife, Ritva. Their two children are named Katja and Ilse. They live in Lapland on a reindeer farm that has been in Olavi's family for generations. Last June, Olavi was involved in a car accident that shattered his hip. He also sustained other significant injuries. He has since undergone several surgeries and will likely have to go through a few more. This has been a very difficult time for his family and community alike. Please speak to the front desk if you are interested in making a donation to help defray Olavi's medical expenses and keep the farm running while he works to recover.

Hannah opened the pamphlet. There was another photo of Olavi and his family, standing in a forest with the sun's orange glow filtering through the pine trees. "Under the Midnight Sun" read the caption. A third photo showed a close-up of the two girls with a reindeer, an animal that was more beautiful than Hannah had expected. There was a section titled: *A Day at the Reindeer Farm,* that detailed the work Olavi and his family had been doing for over a century.

Conner came out of the bathroom a moment later, toweling his hair off with a fluffy organic towel, whistling the rest of the song he had been signing.

"Did you see this?" Hannah asked, holding up the pamphlet. "This guy in Lapland was in an accident. He's a reindeer farmer."

"Wow." Conner took the brochure from her and looked at the pictures. "Great photos."

"You can leave a donation for them at the front desk. Wow, more cool and innovative ideas at this place—TRUISO, hmm ... I wonder if the other rooms are like that, too. Let's stop by the front desk on the way to breakfast." Conner handed the pamphlet back to her and Hannah looked at it one more time before placing it on the table. "I'd like to make a donation."

The organic breakfast was held in their large, organic restaurant with wide French doors that opened onto a terrace and a garden. There was a buffet table set up at the far end of the room, and groups of people sat at large, rustic looking community tables, 10-14 people sitting together at a time—similar to the ones at the restaurant they'd been to last night. The floor was turquoise tile, which gave Hannah the feeling of walking on water. She stopped and looked at the beautiful wall hangings, which were vibrantly colored and geometric-appearing in pattern. She looked more closely and tried to decipher some of the images.

"They're *thangkas,*" a woman said, coming to stand next to her. "They're from Nepal."

"They're beautiful," Hannah said. "I've never seen one before."

"I find them very calming to look at." The woman turned and held out her hand. "I'm Jote, nice to meet you" she said. "Are you enjoying your stay here?"

Hannah smiled and shook her hand. "Yes! Very much! And I was hoping I'd run into you, actually! A friend of yours told me about this place and she said I should talk to you. This is such a great hotel. I just love the concept. I'm so inspired being here, there are so many innovative approaches, tools and services!"

"Thank you Hanna", Jote smiled kindly. "I'm glad you're enjoying yourself here. And what room are you staying in?"

"We're staying in the Lapland room."

"Oh … That's one of my favorites. Well, they're all my favorites, actually."

"Well Jote, would you mind me asking how you got the idea for this place? What was your original vision? It's such a wonderful concept. The harmonic ambiance ... and I really love the idea that people can be helping other people—all the way across the world even, or in some place that they've never heard of—all while they're traveling on vacation or for business. I would love to know what inspired you, what gave you the idea. Would you mind telling me a little bit about it?"

"Sure," Jote said. "My vision was to create a One World chain of hotels and the rooms within the hotels; each room being a representation of a different place in the world is for the purpose of raising awareness of our amazing world's diversity and at the same time brining us back to the awareness of our one-ness, similarity and unity. And it's exactly like you said—they are places that people may have never even heard of before or know anything about. The rooms have pieces, images and artifacts from that place. And then it goes one step further as each room links to various organizations or charities, which we find that are associated with the place. A lot of the time, they're not typical, like the Red Cross or the really big organizations. They tend to be a local family or a person who is in a situation from that place, like in your room. Any donation someone makes to the Lapland room will go directly to Olavi and his family. So the purpose is to create connections between people and support communities despite borders, background, religion or race; to promote sharing, awareness, acceptance, and charity. In addition, our hotels are a place for people to be and get healthy through harmonic ambiance—the TRUISO philosophy."

"That's such an inspiring and impactful idea," Hannah said. "I feel really moved and uplifted just being here. I recently decided to start my own nonprofit. I've been fortunate enough to talk to some other people about what it is exactly I want to be doing, and they've definitely got the wheels turning. And I agree with you; I want to be doing something that will foster the idea of community."

"The sky really is the limit. Maybe even beyond that. Being part of a community, living a healthy lifestyle, they're all just pieces of a large whole. I call it harmonic ambiance."

"Harmonic ambiance," Hannah repeated. "I love that."

"To achieve harmonic ambiance, you engage all the senses and also address nutrition, fitness, living in simple luxury and practicing conscious spirituality. It's health by design. We first address the person's health because when people are healthy and feel balanced, they are able to function at their fullest potential."

"You're totally right," Hannah said. "And you know, that kind of ties in to what I've been thinking about. I have this idea to do something to help people living with traumatic brain injuries. My high school boyfriend—he came with me, actually, he's the tall guy over there with the orange juice—he was in an accident where he suffered a pretty severe head injury and his life just totally changed after that. And I think a lot of people don't realize, that for people suffering from that kind of injury, sometimes the biggest challenge isn't getting better enough to get out of the hospital, but what comes afterward. Trying to figure out how to live life when you're healed enough to be released from the hospital but not necessarily well enough to live life independently."

Jote smiled. "That sounds like a great idea Hannah. And I love that you said you've been meeting all these people.

It's amazing how that works, isn't it? It's like you open yourself up to the possibilities, and things just have a way of happening. You meet the people you need to meet. Every day I do my best to remember to be grateful for everything and truly feel the vibration of appreciation."

"The vibration of appreciation." Hannah smiled. "I like that, too. I like how it sounds and feels ."

"Remember, Hannah. As you breathe in and you breathe out … truth is ONE. Everything is right in front of you."

Hannah nodded slowly, took in a deep breath, taking in what she just heard Jote say; her eyes travelled across the room to Conner, who had just settled himself down at one of the tables and was talking with the woman next to him. "I'm beginning to realize how very true that is Jote," she said. "Thank you so much, it was so wonderful to meet you."

Chapter 12

GO THE DISTANCE

They left San Luis Obispo some time in the late morning and got back onto the Pacific Coast Highway, great billows of fog hanging densely over the ocean, blocking out the sunlight. Conner had his window down and his head leaned back on the headrest.

"Let me ask you something," he said, after they'd driven a little while just listening to the songs on the radio and the wind rushing through the car.

Hannah glanced at him. "Go for it."

"Is there anything that could happen that would make you want to stay at your job?"

"What do you mean?"

"I don't know … say they offered you a raise or a corner office or something. Free cheese Danishes for life."

She laughed. "That's not how it works in publishing."

"You know what I mean, though. What if you had sold that guy's book? The other guy with the messed up head."

"Conner … "

"I guess all I'm try to say is, Han, it makes me happy to think of you out on the East Coast, having a career, doing something I know that you really like. I wish I could have some big important job. I think you're pretty lucky. So it's not that I don't think you should go out there and do what you want. I just wonder if maybe you're feeling discouraged because you didn't sell that book."

Hannah considered this. What if she had sold the book? It would have tided her over for a little while, she suspected, but then she was certain the feeling would come up again. The feeling that though what she was doing was enjoyable and fun, it wasn't what she really wanted.

"No," she said finally. "The answer to your question is no."

He looked at her with a sheepish smile. "I kind of forget my original question."

"If there was anything that would make me stay. It's something deeper than all that other stuff. I mean, I know I go back and forth between being so certain and having my doubts, but this is really something I have to do. And I feel like the people I've been meeting recently, I feel like it's kind of the universe's way of telling me that I'm on the right track. That I'm doing the right thing."

Conner nodded and seemed satisfied with her answer. "Well then, Hannah, babe, if there's anything I can do to help you, let me know."

She reached over and gave his hand a squeeze. "You're already helping. But tell me, what if there was a place that you could've gone to, after you were out of the hospital and trying to adjust to being at home, trying to adjust to life. What would that place look like to you, ideally?"

"Well ... I guess it's kind of changed over the years. When I first got out, I was expecting things to go back to the way they used to be, even though I couldn't totally remember how they used to be. You know, be skating, back to school, go to New York with you. So back then, I was really just looking for someone to help me get my old life back. A lot of people probably feel that way, even if they can't exactly remember what that old life used to be like. But now I think it'd be cool if your organization could help people get used to their new way of life. Whatever that may be. So it's like a better beginning on their new life, rather than just leaving them out there to figure it out on their own. Maybe even just having a time and a place for people to get together, talk about things. You wouldn't ever wish this on anyone, but it always helps to know that you're not the only person going through it."

"I'm sure it does." Hannah was quiet for a minute. "What was that you said? About a better beginning?"

"That it'd be cool if your center could help people get a better beginning. The hospital and outpatient therapy get you so far, but then there's actual life to continue living.

I know I kind of felt like I was starting this on my own, and I wasn't always sure what to do."

"Better Beginnings," Hannah said, trying the two words out. "Conner, I think that's the perfect name. You just named the organization. How do you think it sounds?"

"Better Beginnings?" He grinned. "Why, I think it sounds pretty good, if I do say so myself."

They got to San Diego in the early evening, and after relaxing at the house for a little while, they went out to her sister's restaurant for dinner and to say hello to Mathias, who was working. He came out from the kitchen and sat with them while they feasted on the Wednesday night special—mussels and frites in a white sauce.

"So, Kate tells me you guys are going to accompany her to the race tomorrow," Mathias said.

"We are," Hannah said. She licked the salt from her fingertips. "Wow, these are delicious. I'm not going to be running, though."

"Yes, well," Mathias said, "I might not originally be from this country, but I can't get used to the idea of spending Thanksgiving Day doing anything but preparing food or eating food."

"Mathias's two greatest joys in life," Kate said, laughing. She turned to him. "If anything, it makes sense to get out there and move around some before you go home and stuff yourself silly. Right?"

He held up his hands. "I'm not saying it doesn't. Luckily, you've got me to stay at home and get all the food ready for you to stuff yourself silly with."

"The thought of you slaving away over a hot stove will be like the carrot dangling in front of my face."

Mathias grinned and stood up. "That's all I wanted to hear." He looked at Hannah and Conner. "My sixth sense is telling me that they need me back in the kitchen, but can I send anything else out?"

"We'll take some more mussels, if you've got them" Conner said. "I was wrong to think a burger was the only thing that went with French fries."

"I'll have some more of the garlic breadsticks," Hannah said. She smiled at her sister. "I figure I better carbo load if I'm doing this race tomorrow, right?"

Hannah felt exhilarated the next morning, as she walked with Conner and thousands of other people. She was surprised how many people were there, some running, some walking, everyone clearly having a good time. Kate had gone on ahead with a few members from her running group, promising to meet Hannah and Conner at the finish line.

To Hannah's right, between the buildings, she caught glimpses of the ocean, the waves rolling gently up the beach and back. A gentle breeze ruffled the palm tree fronds back and forth above her, and she looked up and took a deep breath, thinking how different this Thanksgiving was than she ever could have had in New York.

"I could be happy spending every Thanksgiving like this," she said, taking a deep breath.

"Maybe we should make it a new tradition," Conner said. He pushed his sunglasses back and squinted up ahead. "In fact, I think I even see the Thanksgiving turkey way up there."

Only toward the end did Hannah's feet start to ache a little. When she and Conner reached the finish line they each received a medal and a high five.

"Good job!" said the girl who handed Hannah her medal. She gave her a big smile and Hannah smiled back, surprised at how proud of herself she felt for making it to the finish line.

The area at the end of the finish line was crowded, and it took them a little while to find Kate. Hannah figured her sister must've finished quite a while ago, because she didn't appear winded at all.

"How was it?" Kate asked, walking over to them. "Pretty fun, huh?"

"I told Hannah this should be our new Thanksgiving tradition," Conner said. "Maybe you can help me convince her."

"It was fun," Hannah said. "Maybe the last thing I ever expected to do on Thanksgivng Day, but definitely worth it. Did I tell you I met the guy that started this?"

Kate shook her head. "No, I don't think so. Or actually—yeah, maybe you did. When you called and asked me if I'd ever done it before."

"Yeah. I actually ended up meeting him after Brandon took me to hear Frank Shankwitz speak. I was wondering if I might see him. Though I doubt he'd remember me."

"Did you happen to see the guy running in the turkey costume?"

"I did."

"That was Richard."

Hannah laughed. "Really? I totally didn't recognize him."

"Well, you probably weren't expecting him to be in a turkey costume, but now you know for next time. What do you say we start heading back to the house? I'm starving, and I'm sure Mathias could use my help in the kitchen. The man is a culinary genius but his cranberry sauce never comes out right."

They started walking toward the car, the medal Hannah received thumping lightly against her chest. "Kate!" she heard someone calling behind them. She stopped and turned, saw a man she didn't recognize.

"Hey," Hannah said to her sister. "Someone's calling you."

Kate turned and looked and then a smile crossed her face. "Hey, Tim!" she said. "I was hoping we'd run into you! My sister's in town. This is Hannah, and her friend,

Conner. This is Tim Murphy. We met Tim back when we were opening Oasis. I'd say you were the first person who actually believed in what we were doing and knew how to make it happen!"

"It was easy to see that you guys believed in what you were doing," he said with a smile. "Did everyone have a good run today?"

"Some of us walked," Hannah said. "But it was a very pleasant walk!"

"I love that all these people are out here, getting exercise on Thanksgiving," Tim said. "It's such the opposite of what you'd generally see with very few people out exercising as they are so busy with their lives that they do not take the time for themselves to reenergize their day. You just ran a great race and one you can be proud of even when you go back and stuff yourself on that Thanksgiving Day turkey, stuffing and pie."

"Hannah, Tim has actually started a company called PHresh Kitchen," Kate said. "Which is an idea I totally love, and kind of wish I thought of first!" She looked at Tim. "My sister's decided to change careers and start her own organization. Do you have any good advice you'd want to share? You were so helpful when Mathias and I were first starting out, and showing us how to think of the future of the company, not just open our business and hope the business will take off. But actually making a plan for our success. We can't thank you enough for coaching us through the process."

Tim smiled. "Thanks, Kate. What kind of business are you starting, Hannah?"

"It's a nonprofit to help people who have sustained a traumatic brain injury. It's still very much in the beginning stages, but I've been talking with people and getting some really good advice."

"That sounds great. Good health is so important. That's one of my passions, actually. I'd like to help people refocus on becoming healthier through diet and exercise. Eating well and exercising isn't just so you'll look good. I've been running marathons for the past five or six years and have lost 50 pounds by doing so. I've now gotten to a point in my life where just running a marathon is not enough. I am now running multiple marathons over a weekend. I now have ran a half marathon on Saturday and then a full marathon on Sunday for 39.3 miles in two days, twice in the past two years at Walt Disney World in Orlando, Florida called the Goofy Challenge. And I've got to admit the challenge is pretty goofy, but when you run on behalf of a good cause like I did last year for JDRF, the Juvenile Diabetes Research Foundation, and my son, Troy, who is type-1 diabetic, the challenge does not seem too goofy, but just the right thing to do. In fact, I am now signed up to run four races at Walt Disney World in Orlando over four days for a total of 48.6 miles on behalf of JDRF in January of next year called the

Dopey Challenge. I am sure that I will feel pretty dopey half way through the marathon on the final day, but what will get me through the race is the overwhelming feeling of pride knowing that I helped a great cause and my son Troy. But as an added benefit, just knowing that so few people will ever get to accomplish running 48.6 miles, let alone try the Dopey Challenge, just feels fantastic. I feel I have to keep challenging myself by running longer distances and in more unique locations and situations, but not just for the sheer challenge of it, but to give back in some way. So, like you, I am creating a nonprofit called Run 2 End Obesity to educate and teach people and businesses how to eat less and move more. I feel there is a big disconnect between wellness programs and actual places to eat. The wellness programs do a great job of teaching what to eat and how to exercise, but they don't do a good job of tying together where to eat. Hence, why I created PHresh Kitchen."

"I hope one day that through PHresh Kitchen and Run 2 End Obesity, we can significantly reduce or eliminate obesity and aid in the reduction of health-related issues and extend individuals' lives. We are only here on Earth for a short time, and I believe that everyone has the ability to exercise in some way to allow them to live out their own life's marathon. I truly believe that life is a marathon and you must experience life to its fullest. That means taking risks that others believe you should not be taking or that they will not do for themselves. That means putting your neck out there even if other people think you are crazy. And I've found through marathon running, that marathons are a good metaphor for life. You can't give up if you want to run a marathon. You must train and practice. You must eat properly and stay hydrated. So you cannot think that you are going to instantly go out and conquer the world or run a marathon. You must start slow, but with a defined plan. You first have to walk. Then walk some more. Jog a little. Walk a little. Try running a little faster. Walk if you need to, but continue to run and before you know it you will be able to run some very long distances like a marathon.

"You are following the right steps and processes to see how to create your successful traumatic brain injury nonprofit. You are asking for advice from various people and that is great! But I have to caution you that to be truly successful in creating your nonprofit is to make sure you ask for the correct advice. You see, just like running a marathon or creating a business, you will have a lot of people ask you along the way, 'Why do you want to waste your time doing that?' They do not understand your motivation or your desire. They don't want to experience what you are doing or walk in your footsteps. Or they just don't care to hear what you have to say. You have to block out the negativity, focus on the positive and create your overriding mission of why you want to do what you want to do. It will guide you during the rough times. You have to be willing to avoid and eliminate the negative people in your life and focus on your mission. And you have to tell yourself that it is okay to avoid and eliminate those negative people in your life. A wise lady taught me that only 30% of the people you meet will like you and your ideas. The 70% could care less about you and your ideas. So stop trying to impress and get approval from everyone, and that includes your friends and family. Focus your intentions on your mission and good fortune will follow.

"And if you want to be successful in business—whether it's a nonprofit or franchising a business—you can't give up there, either. Along the way, it might be really tempting to just throw the towel in. It might seem like way too much effort or just something you can't do or too many people are telling you that you can't do it or that you are crazy. But nothing beats that feeling when you cross the finish line in a marathon. It's even a different experience than running a 5K or 10K race. A marathon, like creating a business or nonprofit, tests your true will, your true friends and family, and your real mental capacity. And in a franchise business, like a nonprofit, you need to be focused on your client and do whatever it takes to create a long-term plan, like the plan you need to train for and run a marathon, which will give you the greatest success in the shortest amount of time. So I guess what it really comes down to is: will you go the distance to make it happen and avoid all of the distractions?"

"I still remember you telling that to Mathias and me, the first time we met you," Kate said. "It's such a great phrase.

Especially because you can apply it to running, to business, to pretty much anything."

"Exactly. And try to never go against your core values of honesty and integrity. That might sound obvious, but it can be easy to get caught up in the moment, especially if you find yourself having to work with someone who doesn't share the same values you do. And sometimes this requires that you really step back and evaluate the people in your life. You don't know somebody until you know someone. If you come across those people, disassociate yourself from them as quickly as possible. Sometimes in life, you do not get to change the current circumstances as quickly as you would like, but make all the efforts to do so, even if it seems crazy, stupid or unfathomable to others, including your friends and family. You don't need mental anguish like that in your life from unscrupulous or dishonest people. I've had bosses who did not view business the same way I did and twice made offers to buy them out of their company though private equity firms. I've watched bosses figure a way around the system to satisfy their own personal needs in spite of their partners' interest and investment in the company. I've personally had partners that were interested in the quick dollar, which was going against the dream of really building a sustainable company. Then finally one day I had a good friend and advisor named John, who asked me very point-blank questions, such as, 'Why are you attracting these negative individuals into your life? What is causing or allowing these people to come into your life? And what are you doing to prevent these people from entering your life again?' His questions hit a nerve with me as I thought long and hard about his questions. But then I realized that he was correct. I was allowing these individuals into my life. I was allowing them to affect my thoughts and behaviors to suit their way of thinking and going away from my core values. What I realized was that I believed that others around me had my best interests at heart. That these individuals actually cared about what I was thinking and that they truly believed in what I was doing. But they were not. They cared about their dreams, what was in it for them and not of a cooperative environment. So now I remind myself often, 'the only person that I can change is myself.' I cannot change anyone, except my associations. I cannot dictate others' choices, but I can definitely change myself. I always get to choose who I hang out with. And so do you! So when you find yourself in an association that does not appear to be correct, or that others are out for themselves, disassociate yourself with them as quickly as possible. Seek those who want to help you grow through a cooperative environment and not a competitive environment. You will save yourself a lot of time and money, which will allow you to get closer to your dreams quicker with those who actually want to cooperate with you!"

"That's really good advice," Hannah said. In the publishing world, she'd had the good fortune to mostly work with people who shared similar values and ethics, though there had been a few individuals she'd tried to disassociate herself from because she hadn't agreed with the way they'd gone about doing things. "What is PHresh Kitchen about? It sounds interesting. It seems like I've met a lot of people lately who have some really innovative and interesting businesses. The hotel Conner and I stayed at a few nights ago was really cool. Each room represented a different place in the world and told you a story about some of the inhabitants there. It's so inspiring to hear about everyone's different ideas."

"Well, PHresh Kitchen is pretty simple, actually, and I could talk for days on what I believe PHresh Kitchen will do for the food service industry." Tim said. "After I got into marathon running, I realized that there were very few fast, casual, freshly prepared and healthful dining options that served the trend of eating low-calorie and healthful foods, and even fewer options that were an inexpensive investment for franchises and people who wanted to be business owners. So I created a fast-casual food and beverage company that capitalizes on the consumer trend to eat low-calorie and healthful foods. PHresh Kitchen uses smaller modular stores, which translates into lower entry costs and more location options than competitors. PHresh Kitchen reduces risk with high volume, contracted, replicated locations, swift ramp-up of revenue, flexible, multiple menus and real-time, cloud-based systems. PHresh Kitchen can quickly lead this food industry segment by providing one of the industry's highest sales-to-investment ratios and we have multiple menus, which allows us to compete with multiple organizations on multiple levels. For instance, Subway restaurants is building over 3,000 stores this year alone worldwide, but they are building that with just one standard menu. PHresh Kitchen has multiple menus and a much cheaper entry point than many competitors, thus reducing investor risk and adding flexibility to our offering. So we believe if positioned correctly, we will have a total of $500MM+ in sales and 1,000 units within the next five years."

"Wow! You're kidding!" Hannah said.

"It's pretty incredible when you hear it put out like that, huh?" Kate said.

"Just so you know, I've spent my career in franchising and hospitality. I've gotten to work for some of the world's largest franchise and restaurant companies. I first started and learned practical mom and pop entrepreneurial experience while working for my late father, Al Murphy, and with my mother, Jean Murphy, in their many businesses in New Jersey since I was eight years old. I had the opportunity to work in their fencing, construction, welding, restaurant, arcade, miniature golf and growing hydroponic businesses. The hydroponic produce business was well before EPCOT opened in Orlando, Florida with the Land Pavillion. Later in life I was mentored by one of the greatest franchisors of all time. His name was Abe Gustin, Jr., and the former chairman and CEO of Applebee's International. He built 100 Applebee's casual dining restaurants a year for over ten years, and I spent four years with him asking him how he built such a great company while I was his chief financial officer for the central Florida Applebee's franchise. However, I have also learned what not to do by some of the ... not so great franchise companies. So I have a deep perspective, appreciation and understanding of what it takes to be a successful franchise company from the top of the business at 30,000 feet to the bottom of the business, and everywhere in between.

"The lesson that I learned the most in the franchising business is that everything is about the franchisee and the success of the franchisee. And I truly believe that businesses and individuals can achieve far greater success and wealth through franchising than you can with any other business structure. Mom and pops, company owned- and licensed businesses, do not have the same ability to grow quickly using OPM—other people's money—and retain the control of the concept's brand through arm's length third-party agreements as franchising can provide. And since I was the former CFO of some of the companies that I work for, I also discovered while working with various finance and private equity firms, that if a company decides to sell, companies are usually valued more as a franchisor than most other business combinations. So starting PHresh Kitchen seemed like the perfect synthesis of the two things that are very important to me: good low-calorie and healthful foods, combined with the best business model of franchising and a low-cost entry point for the investor that can deliver success and wealth for the long term.

"However, I decided not to stop with PHresh Kitchen, as I see that a lot of other businesses and individuals need the same franchising help in creating their companies, too. Thus, I created another company called Advanced Franchise Systems, Inc. There are a lot of self-proclaimed gurus and experts in the franchising field that charge excessive amounts of money, but don't have the top-to-bottom approach that I give to franchise companies from working as a former CFO. So I teach clients how to franchise faster and more efficiently to maintain control over their brand, instead of licensing or growing their brand through corporate expansion. I coach the mental focus shift, from corporate unit success, to the success of franchisees. Abe Gustin, who I discussed earlier, taught me those principles. I find it hard to believe that if Abe Gustin did not have those principles, Applebee's would not be as successful today. His focus on the franchisee allowed Applebee's to grow at one point to over 100 new units a year for nearly ten years, and today Applebee's is still the largest casual dining chain in the world, with over 2,000 restaurants. So once the franchisees are successful using excellent operations, prototypes, systems and procedures, then the franchisor—if planned correctly—should be successful for the long haul by creating wealth for the franchisor. There are many restaurant examples today like Applebee's and Subway, but franchising does not stop with restaurants. Franchising is everywhere we look, like service businesses, hotels, rental companies, convenience stores, automotive stores and yes, of course, restaurants. In fact, there are over 120 different types of franchise businesses. And creating PHresh Kitchen into a franchise business only seemed natural to me."

"We'd totally consider PHresh Kitchen, if we had not already built Oasis. However, I think we will be calling you in the future to help us franchise Oasis with Advanced Franchise Systems. Tim, you have such a great background in both franchising and the ability to help and grow companies," Kate said. "I think PHresh Kitchen is such a great idea, and there's definitely a need for it now. It sounds like you are a few years ahead of the curve."

"Kate, I really believe that we have a great ultra-marathon ahead! As we spoke before, my mission is to help reduce obesity through diet and exercise, and educating guests to eat less and move more. I also believe that if Subway can build over 3,000 restaurants this year alone worldwide and remain the world's largest franchise company with one menu and one brand, what could PHresh Kitchen do with an even lower investment than a Subway restaurant store with multiple menus, multiple revenue streams and controlled by the World Wide Web under one brand? And, I believe that if you educate people and businesses on the positives of eating healthy and exercising often, as we will be doing with Run 2 End Obesity, and couple that with PHresh Kitchen in providing low-calorie and healthful foods in high-volume locations using modular units, and use education to compliment both, then yes, I believe that we will have great success ahead!"

They parted ways with Tim a few minutes later and headed back to Kate's house, where Hannah hoped Mathias would have a big Thanksgiving dinner waiting for them.

Chapter 13

HABITS AND ATTITUDES

They left San Diego on Saturday and stayed overnight in the little town of San Simeon. It was raining when they woke up, so they had breakfast at a coffee shop and then got back on the road. They decided they'd stop and get a late lunch in San Francisco, and then make the final leg of the trip back up to the North Bay. The rain had stopped by the time they reached Half Moon Bay, and by the time they they'd reached South San Francisco, the clouds had broken up and the sun was shining brightly. By some stroke of very good luck, Hannah managed to find a parking spot right on 18th and Dolores. She parked the car easily in what was rather a tight spot, and they got out and stood on the sidewalk for a minute, arms stretched above their heads toward the blue sky. Hannah's back cracked pleasantly and she twisted her upper body one way, then the other. Conner let his head fall back and he took a deep breath, a smile on his face.

"I love this city," he said.

They walked down the sidewalk toward his favorite pizza place. Across the street was the place that made, in Hannah's opinion, the best ice cream in the world, and she made a note to swing over there and pick up a pint of the salted caramel, which was her absolute favorite.

She was still daydreaming about how good that ice cream would be when she saw a man walking toward them, looking at them as though he knew who they were, though she had no idea who he was. He held his hand up to her, like he wanted a high five. She stopped and looked at him quizzically. He had short, dark hair, and a handsome face; he looked like someone she'd gone to college with though she was pretty certain this was not that guy. Or was it? Why else would he be offering his hand to her?

"I think he wants you to high five him," Conner whispered, nudging her. "Come on, you can't leave the guy hanging."

"Uh …" She glanced quizzically from Conner back to the guy again.

If she had been by herself she might've just kept walking. But since Conner was there, and the guy had a smile on his face, she reached over and gave him a high five.

"I don't think I've ever high fived a stranger before," Hannah said.

The man smiled. "Most people haven't. I try to high five at least five strangers before noon. It's a fun challenge. Think you're up for it?"

"No," Hannah said, at the same time Conner said, "Sure."

The man laughed. "So I bet you think there's probably no way you could high-five five total strangers?" He looked at Conner. "You've probably high fived a stranger before."

"Actually, I have," Conner said. "And it kind of made their day."

"Exactly." The man held out his hand. "I'm Erik Swanson. And one of the awesome things about high fiving strangers is that you actually end up meeting a lot of really cool people in the process."

"I think that's awesome you make it a habit to high five strangers," Conner said. "You know, I can remember how completely surprised and then how happy the person was that I randomly high fived. I don't even remember why I did it, but I can still remember the huge smile they gave me. It just seemed like a pretty cool way to help someone feel better, even if it was just for that moment, even if you didn't end up actually talking to them."

Erik nodded. "Exactly," he said. "It's such a simple gesture, yet it can make a big difference. Like your friend said, it can really help someone feel happier. I'd like to see people be happier with their habits and attitudes. There's so much negativity in the world and it's easy to let that infiltrate your life. I want people to be able to smile and have the courage to smile all the time, even in adversity."

"Habits and attitudes," Hannah said. "It can be really hard to change those."

"It can. But it's well worth the effort. And the two really go hand in hand. I like to think of them as *habitudes*. And there's secret habitudes, did you know?"

"No, I didn't."

"I facilitate training sessions that can help you change your habits and your attitude."

"Oh yeah? And is high fiving strangers a part of that? I get the idea of it, but really, I think it'd just end up making me feel like a fool." She could see herself trying to high five someone and having them look at her like she was crazy, or, worse, completely ignore her.

"It's going to do a few things. First, you're making a commitment to do something. Committing yourself to something and then following through is a habit that will serve you well in whatever it is you decide to do. And then you're getting out there, meeting new people. When you don't branch out and constantly see the same people day after day, you're staying stagnant. You're not growing or moving; you're just getting the same advice and opinions and that's going to prevent you from getting to the next level."

"Okay, that makes sense but I still don't think I'm going to be able to just walk up to five complete strangers and high five them."

Erik smiled. "I bet you could. And for the person you're high fiving? It could make someone's day. Think of it as random acts of awesomeness. Which brings me to the next thing I think might help you. Remind yourself to P.E.A."

Conner laughed. Hannah stared. "Excuse me?"

"P.E.A, as in P-E-A, or be positive, energetic, and awesome."

"Unfortunately, I think I am none of those."

"Ah, but you are. Maybe not all the time, but everyone has the potential, and you just need to remind yourself of it. Make it your top-of-mind awareness, and literally remind yourself to be positive, energetic, and awesome. I think you'll start noticing things just start turning for the better. It's always easier to think negative thoughts, but reminding yourself to be positive, energetic, and awesome, is going to go a long way in changing your habits and attitudes. And you want to know one other thing you could try? I call it the sixty-second morning mirror. Start every morning off like this, if you can. Look in the mirror. Look yourself right in the eye. Have a little conversation, pump yourself up for the rest of the day. Remind yourself to be positive, energetic, and awesome. Visualize how you'd like to see the rest of your day go. By starting the day off on a positive note, you're setting the stage for what is to come. And sure, that's not to say bad things won't come up—they very well might. If you pump yourself up in the morning and give yourself those reminders and those affirmations right from the start, it can transform your day. It's like you constantly have these reminders, keeping you on track. It can be something like, *I will succeed.* Or, *I believe in myself.* It's good to keep them simple."

"You sound like a good guy to have around," Hannah said. "You know, reminding me of all the little things that I should carry with me throughout the day."

"All you need to do is change your habits and attitude. Which can take time, of course. But if you're committed to making those changes—it'll happen. Always smile and have the courage to smile, even in adversity. I know that might sound a little cheesy, but it's true."

"Speaking of cheesy," Conner said. "I am starving. We were just gonna go grab some pizza—want to join us?"

"I've got a talk to give at the Moscone Center in front of about 7,000 graduating students to share some awesome principles of the 'Habitude Success for the Real Life', so I've got to get down there, otherwise I would have definitely joined you guys. But, you two enjoy your lunch." He started to walk off but then turned, caught Hannah's eye. "I bet you can high five at least two strangers by the time you're done eating."

Hannah couldn't help but return his smile. "We'll see," she said.

She spent her last three days in California relaxing and trying not to think about returning to New York. Sometimes, it was difficult to remember why she wanted to leave, especially on a day like this when it was nearly December and still mild enough for short sleeves, and she could sit out on the deck with Conner and watch the last of the leaves fall from the grape vines.

The night before she was to leave, Hannah had dinner at home with her parents. They seemed to touch on every subject but work, so as the meal wound down, Hannah took a sip of wine, set her glass down, and looked at her parents.

"I was hoping we could talk about this a little before I left," she said. "I know you guys don't necessarily agree with what it is I'm doing, but I hope you can still be supportive and understand that I'm doing this because I want to help people, and because I want to be doing something that really matters to me."

Her parents were silent for a moment. Her father picked up his napkin and wiped the corners of his mouth. He took a sip of wine and leaned back in his chair.

"Your mom and I have been talking, Hannah," he said. "And while I'm sure you can understand that you deciding to change careers is a surprise, we also believe you should be doing something you truly love."

"We only want what's best for you," her mom said. "And if this is something you feel strongly about, and something that you want to do, then of course we absolutely support you. And we're excited to see how it turns out."

Hannah felt her shoulders relax in relief. She smiled. "Did I tell you I've got a name for it?"

"That's great!" her mom said. "What is it?"

"Better Beginnings. It was Conner's idea, actually."

"Better Beginnings. I love it."

Her father held up his wine glass and toasted her. "To you," he said. "And your organization, that it may be prosperous and bring you all the happiness you deserve."

"Thank you, Dad," Hannah said, picking up her own glass.

Mrs. Tero drove them down to the airport. She let them out at the passenger drop off and told Conner she'd circle around a few times and pick him up after he walked Hannah to security.

"I'm really glad you made it out here," he said. They held hands as they walked past the long lines of people waiting to check their luggage. Hannah felt an ache in her throat. She wanted time to stop, she didn't want to get on the plane.

"I'm glad I did, too," she said. They passed a newsstand and a coffee shop, and the air filled with the aroma of burnt coffee and toast. Hannah stopped, her eyes filling with tears. She started to hide her face but then stopped, recalling, suddenly, that encounter with Jason Munson in the café, when she'd been sitting there crying and feeling like a fool and he told her it was okay. She brought her hand down and looked at Conner.

"I don't want to leave," she said.

He brought his hand up to the side of her face. "Then stay. But you know you want to go back. I can see it in your eyes. Maybe I can come visit."

"I don't want to leave you here. Can you come with me? If I figure out a way for you to come, would you do that?"

"You know I would in a second. But ... it's more complicated than that. I'll definitely come for a visit."

"I wish things didn't have to be so complicated. They really aren't."

Conner laughed. "We sound like the world's most dysfunctional couple."

"Okay, not complicated then ... a challenge."

He tucked a tendril of hair behind her ear and let out a sigh. "Everything is a challenge."

"I hate to hear you say that." Her eyes started to fill with tears again.

"Hey." He lifted her chin so she was looking at him, his handsome face blurry behind her tears. She wiped at her eyes. He smiled. "Don't be sad. I like a good challenge. Almost as much as I like you. You're going to be just fine, Hannah. Call me when you get in, okay? So I know you got in safely."

She nodded and gave him a hug, wished there was some way she could be on both coasts at the same time. "I will."

Chapter 14

GRAB A HAND

There were about a dozen people ahead of her in line at the taxi stand. Hannah stood, clutching her suitcase, staring at the rain as it lashed the pavement. The air was cold and the murkiness of the day matched the way she felt inside. She'd been able to sleep for a few hours on the flight back, though when she woke up she was disoriented and couldn't remember if she was coming or going. But now, she was back on the East Coast, and it was time to follow through with everything she said she was going to do. Except it suddenly seemed like an insurmountable challenge. There was a very large difference, she was beginning to realize, between saying you were going to do something and then actually going through the motions and doing it. Was she supposed to go quit her job tomorrow and just dive right in to opening this nonprofit? She had enough in savings that she could do this, if she could get things going. And she knew, she knew without a doubt, that if she told herself she'd open it while continuing to be an agent, that she would never do it.

A lone taxi drove up and a middle-aged woman climbed in. The line crept forward.

"Terrible day to try to get a cab," the man said standing next to her.

"I feel like it's a terrible day for a lot of things," Hannah said, still watching the rain. She glanced at him. "I'm sorry; that was rude."

"Are you just returning from someplace warm and tropical?" he asked with a smile.

"Well … sort of. I was visiting family in California."

"That sounds nice." He held out his hand. "I'm Scott Duffy."

"Hannah."

"Nice to meet you. So you had a nice trip?"

"I did. Part of me kind of wishes I could just stay there. It just … it felt easier out there. Everything felt easier. I'm sort of about to embark on a big life change, I guess, and it seemed totally doable while I was out in California, but now that I'm back and actually have to do something … I'm not so sure." She laughed weakly. "And reality comes crashing back down. I know what I've got to do, but I'm so afraid the whole thing's going to blow up in my face. That it's not going to work out and turn into this huge failure."

"The path to success is always littered with failure," the man told her. "What is it that you're about to do?"

"I'm going to start a nonprofit. And I've spent the past few weeks thinking about it and speculating about it and now is the time to do something about it. I guess I was thinking that once I decided to do it, I wouldn't feel scared anymore. But I realize that's kind of silly."

"One of the things I've learned is the times when I needed the most help or had the most struggle was that there was always someone who reached out with a hand. When someone reaches out that hand, it's your job to grab it. It isn't always the easiest thing to do, either."

"It is hard asking for help," Hannah admitted. "I actually probably know a lot of people who'd be more than willing to help, if they could. It's just really hard to let go of the idea that you're going to have to fail sometimes. That you're not going to be able to do everything right, all the time."

"Sometimes I ask people: 'how many times in your life have you been doing everything right?' For example, as a businessperson, you've written the right plan, you executed it perfectly, you did everything that you were taught to do. Or you're a parent and you give everything that you have to your child, hoping that he or she has a great life. Or there was a social cause and you gave everything, you put your heart and soul into making this happen. And then something out of nowhere came and knocked you completely off course."

Hannah blanched, thinking about Conner. "That sounds more familiar than you know," she said.

He looked at her closely. "And maybe when it happens it feels like the worst thing ever."

"It did. It still does."

"You've got to look at it like this, Hannah: You have good days, you have bad days. But you'll never know which is which until some time way down the line because you don't know what you'll make of the experience. And maybe you're still at a point now where it seems like that's still a really bad thing, whatever it is that happened, but it could just be you haven't gone far enough yet, in whatever it is you're supposed to be doing. It could be that at some point down the road you look back and realize that maybe what happened at the time didn't seem like a good thing, but it helped get you to the place you are now." He reached into his coat pocket and pulled out his phone. "I'm going to give you the contact info for a friend of mine. He's a CPA, and he's worked with a lot of nonprofit startups. He'll be able to help you. Not saying you have to use his services necessarily, but he'll be able to point you in the right direction, and answer any questions you might have about the financial end of things."

Hannah got her own phone out and entered the information as Scott read it to her. They were almost to the front of the line. She took a deep breath and felt some of the tension in her neck and shoulders ease.

"This is you, reaching out your hand to help me, huh," she said, putting her phone in her purse. "Thank you."

Scott smiled and patted her on the shoulder. "See? It doesn't have to be hard to take someone's hand when they're offering it. Good luck with everything, Hannah."

The next day, Hannah went into work and gave her notice. She knew from the research she'd done the night before that she had a lot to do to get her nonprofit started and there was no way she could continue to work and do that at the same time. She stayed on for another week, calling her clients, all of who seemed genuinely surprised at her departure. Though she hadn't been able to sell his book, she phoned Victor and Mae and told them about her plans.

"Can we make a donation to your nonprofit?" Mae asked. "It would be an honor if you'd let us do that."

Hannah swallowed the lump in her throat. "Of course you can," she said. "You guys would be the first, actually."

The last day at the office, she stood, looking out the window a final time. She felt less sad than she expected; Brandon had been promoted to junior agent and Hannah knew it would only be a matter of time until he was a senior agent. If anyone was going to take her place, she was glad it was him.

The next day, she called Chris Oliver, the CPA, and told him Scott Duffy had given her his number. He went through the various forms and applications she'd have to fill out and though most were available online, he said he'd send her hard copies in the mail. He also gave her the name of a friend of his who was a commercial realtor and might be able to help her find a good place to rent. She wrote the woman's information down, and as she did so, she silently thanked Scott again for offering her his help.

Chapter 15

GIVE, BELIEVE, RECEIVE

It was a cold, clear day, the sky was a piercing blue and her breath billowed out in little clouds as she walked. Hannah passed storefronts decorated for Christmas and people carrying several shopping bags in each hand. She figured this year she might just get her Christmas shopping done on time, though every store she went into was packed, the checkout lines were long, the people seemed overly impatient, and finding that one perfect item amongst so many others suddenly seemed impossible.

She stood in front of a display of beautiful silk scarves and wondered which color her sister might prefer, except that her sister didn't wear scarves. A very stylish and petite, dark-haired woman came and stood next to her and then pulled down a charcoal-colored scarf.

"You made that look easy," Hannah said. "I feel like I've been standing here for the past fifteen minutes and I still can't make a decision. I can't decide which scarf my sister would like, or if she'd even wear a scarf, at all. Usually, I like the Christmas season, but this year I feel a bit overwhelmed and not in the spirit. In fact, I've noticed over the course of my trip that many people out shopping lack the kind of holiday spirit I felt this morning, after deciding I'd take care of my Christmas shopping today. Wow. I'm so sorry. I must be exhausting you."

The woman smiled. "How about you come with me for a coffee? I was supposed to meet up with a friend, but she had to cancel a few minutes ago. There's this great little café that roasts their own beans we were going to check out, just around the block. You look like you could use a little treat and some holiday cheer."

"No, that's—" Hannah stopped. Before deciding to shop, she'd spent the morning holed up in her apartment, researching startup grants for nonprofits and felt like she hadn't had a real conversation all day, much less a little joy by the holiday shopping break. "You know what? That sounds great. Yes, let's go."

The woman's name was Monique Laurette, and after she paid for the scarf, she and Hannah went around the block and got rich, aromatic coffees and gingerbread scones.

"I always hate to see people get so stressed out during the holiday season," Monique said. "It should be such a joyful time but a lot of people seem to get caught up in the rushing around, buying presents, and trying to find the perfect one. More and more, people seem way too overwhelmed."

"That's me," Hannah said. "This year, anyway. Usually I enjoy Christmas; just the spirit of it, not necessarily the gift buying. That seems to get more and more over the top every year. Which, when you're a kid is great, but every year it seems to get more and more ridiculous and have less meaning. There used to be a real joy in it—in the giving and receiving."

Monique took a sip of her coffee and nodded. "I agree," she said. "In fact, I think there's a new kind of spirituality emerging, where the parameters of religious doctrine are too limiting for many. The unfortunate thing is when it comes to Christmas we feel that we can no longer call it that as a society, because "Christ" denotes religion, and religious beliefs. Yet so many of us celebrate Christmas or at least the season of giving. The idea of a common spirituality or value of giving can be brought back into this holiday. Christmas has lost much of its specialness and meaning because we don't know how to talk about it in the context of a broader spirituality. We find ourselves avoiding saying 'Merry Christmas,' as it might offend someone or be politically incorrect. We also get caught up in the 'have to' and all the expectations we believe others have—even our own."

"It's kind of depressing, actually. Which totally isn't how it should be." Hannah sighed, remembering the various Christmases of her own childhood, how she and Kate would try to stay up all night but would end up falling asleep on the floor at the top of the stairs. There was something special about being a child and believing in and feeling that magic.

Monique smiled as though she could hear Hannah's thoughts. "Do you remember as a kid the magic of Santa Claus? How exciting it was to go to bed on Christmas Eve and imagine he was going to be showing up some time in the night, with his sleigh and reindeer and sack of presents that you tried to be good for all year? There is magic in that idea, and as a child, it's really a thrilling thing. But parents don't know how to tell their kids that Santa is more of a beautiful idea and a spirit, rather than a real person."

"I remember asking my mom if Santa was real. I think I was in third or fourth grade. And I remember the way she kind of stuttered, then didn't say anything, and then totally changed the subject by asking me if I wanted to bake Christmas cookies." Hannah laughed. "That's one of the most vivid memories I have of my mother, actually. There was just this understanding between us that I now knew Santa Claus was not real. There was never a discussion about this huge shift in belief. As a kid, this shift was an enormous let down, to say the least."

"And your mom's reaction is typical. Parents really aren't equipped with the tools to communicate the magic of Santa and that it's actually a more wonderful thing to know about the spirit of giving and gratitude, which are very important in this emerging spirituality. The discussion should be a rite of passage. But most parents don't know how to communicate this, so they wait for their kids to find out at school or figure it out for themselves. Kids don't like to tell the parents that they don't believe because they don't want that experience to end. But really, it should be this wonderful thing about believing in the magic of giving and receiving. That thrilling feeling of being special and being celebrated shouldn't go away, but get bigger when you share the idea of also bringing this to others. Most parents do not know how to tell their child about Santa and make it a powerful experience. Honestly, we need to figure out how to remind ourselves, too."

Hannah ran her finger down the handle of her coffee cup. "It's funny how everything is so much different when you're a kid. When it's easy to believe about that kind of stuff, and then, as you get older, it gets harder and harder to feel that magic."

"But it doesn't have to. You can still believe in the magic of Santa, just in a different way. I like to think about the spirit of Santa as an acronym: See Abundance Now Thankfully Always. It's all about believing you are truly surrounded by an abundant universe and feeling gratitude—always. You give, you believe, and you will receive. It's the magic and the full spirit of giving. That belief, and the happiness that comes with it, helps reveal our own unique gift to share with the world. Santa stands for joy, and the magical transformative power of gratitude. So, we can become Santa and aid in bringing that magic into our lives and into the lives of others."

"See Abundance Now Thankfully Always." Hannah smiled and made a mental note to tell Conner about that the next time she talked to him. "That's awesome. And it totally describes what the holiday should be about. It also resonates with me, as I've experienced it with many of the people I've recently met. They seem so giving, and their advice has been like perfect little gifts—gifts I really needed during those moments. I really felt, I don't know, that thrill or joy, which seemed to fill them with joy in return."

"When we live our truth, we manifest our heart's deepest desires and share our unique gift. Our bliss is happiness and happiness is the greatest gift we could give or receive and it's through living our truth and feeling happiness that we are giving back to the world. We need to believe in this power—the more we believe the more we will receive and be able to give to each other. It's really important to embrace this magic." Monique took a sip of coffee and then held the latte mug between her hands. "Your thoughts create your future—so, feel good and always believe. And when you face challenges, recognize each challenge as a gift. Because if you didn't have the challenge, you wouldn't be on an adventure, you wouldn't be getting to a new place, you wouldn't be presented with people and ideas that may make you think differently and lead you to the place you want to be. Say yes to the adventure. Listen to your heart and trust that you will be guided in the right direction—believe."

"But how do you listen to your heart?" Hannah asked.

Monique showed a small smile, like she had asked herself the same question many times. "It's easier said than done. You just have to make it a goal to try and keep a calm mind during uncertain times and see what the universe or divine is trying to teach us. Go beyond the fearful thoughts you might be thinking and believe that you are exactly where you need to be to learn something important or receive the perfect gift. When I come up against obstacles and challenges, and acknowledge I'm getting overwhelmed and negative, I remind myself to get out of my own way. Recognize when you're off balance, stop yourself and have the courage to quiet your mind. Tune into your heart, have gratitude and know that we're always being guided in a better way than we know ourselves. Always believe and feel that love. I try to let go a bit and remind myself that it's not about being loved, it's about being love."

"I'm definitely writing that one down." Hannah pulled a pen from her purse and used one of the napkins. "That's a beautiful phrase. And so true. I think a lot of people forget that. I know I do."

Monique nodded. "It's easy to forget, especially if you're caught up in the moment, like when you are around pushy holiday shoppers. You've got to acknowledge the excuses you have to be angry and the desire to assign blame. We too often choose to be angry and fuel our anger with our thoughts. Sometimes it helps to write a list of your excuses, either on paper or in your head, and then replace each excuse with a positive and more loving truth. And by doing this, we find the ability to move forward feeling really good. We stop letting others' negativity and expectations hold us back. We stop giving too much power to other people's actions and beliefs, waiting for the permission slip."

"I've done that so many times," Hannah said. "But when you put it like that, it sounds so silly."

"It does, doesn't it? And yet, it's so common. Why would we wait for someone else to give us permission to do something that we want to do or to simply feel good? But it's very human to want to be a kid in some way. Everything seemed much easier when we had less responsibility and more imagination—when many of us really believed in Santa Claus."

By the time Hannah finished her coffee, she felt rejuvenated and ready to face a few more stores before going home to get some more work done. She gave Monique a hug before they parted ways. "Thanks so much for inviting me out for coffee," she said. "It was exactly what I needed. It was the perfect gift."

"Have a very merry Christmas, Hannah, and remember to believe."

"I will, Monique. Merry Christmas to you, too."

Chapter 16

NEVER QUIT

Hannah spent the next several days working on her mission statement and experienced what she'd heard many writers say time and time again: *It sounded like a great idea in my head but then I tried to put it down on paper.* Eventually, she closed her laptop and grabbed her legal pad and purse and left the apartment. She hoped all she needed was some fresh air and a change of scenery, so she went to the Ottendorfer Library and sat down at one of the tables. Her thoughts were still as jumbled as the mission statement she was trying to write, though. At the far end of the table, a man sat reading a hardcover book. Hannah recognized the title and the cover art immediately. The man glanced up and saw her watching him.

"Are you enjoying the book?" she asked.

He smiled. "Yes, I am. Have you read it?"

"I have." She knew, in fact, the opening pages by heart. She'd fallen in love with them instantly and knew she would offer representation to the author, who was one of her first clients. "I know the person who wrote the book, actually."

"Well, I'm certainly enjoying it so far. Is it a friend of yours?"

"No. I used to be a literary agent."

"Oh, I see. And what do you do now, if you *used* to be a literary agent?"

Hannah looked down at her jumbled notes. *I'm not sure,* she wanted to say. But instead, she looked back at the man, who had a kind expression on his face. "I'm starting a nonprofit."

"Are you? Tell me about it."

"Well … the idea is to help people who have suffered a traumatic brain injury get the necessary resources to live as independent a life as possible."

"That sounds great. A worthwhile cause."

"Thank you. I'm trying to write the mission statement and it's not going well. To put it mildly."

The man closed the book and set it down. "You sound defeated," he said. "Don't let this defeat you. And it sounds to me you've got your mission statement right there. You just said it to me."

"I did?"

"Sure. Maybe tweak it a little, expand a bit, but a mission statement is supposed to be concise, right? And what you just told me right now is concise and describes exactly what you're going to do."

For a moment, Hannah was silent. "You're right," she finally said. She wrote the sentence down. "Thank you!" she said. "Why didn't I see that before? Why was all this other stuff getting in the way, when it was literally right there? Wow. What is your name?"

"Lynn Barnes."

Hannah moved a few seats down so she was next to him. She shook his hand. "Thanks so much, Lynn. I'm Hannah."

He laughed. "I didn't do anything."

"But you did. I was about to drive myself crazy trying to do this."

"It might feel that way sometimes. But you're doing something you feel strongly about, aren't you? If you have passion and know what your talents and strengths are, if you combine those two and you believe in yourself, you can go off and accomplish whatever it is you set your mind out to do. You can have a life of extreme personal achievement and success by making a choice and living life to the fullest. And you've got to make the decision that you want to live life to the fullest. It's about controlling your mind and your attitude and how you think of yourself and what you bring into your mind as far as education and knowledge that will help you succeed no matter what kind of circumstances come your way."

"I know I need to try to look at the challenges that come up in a more positive way." She thought back to what Conner had said at the airport, how he liked challenges. "I guess I just start to feel afraid that I've made a mistake, that I shouldn't have left my job, that I have no clue what I'm doing, that I'm going to fail." She shook her head. "All that good stuff. Things that I've been feeling for a while now, and they'll go away for a bit but then they always seem to crop back up."

"People tend to let fear get in their way of taking action. They might feel like they're not knowledgeable enough or don't have enough experience to accomplish what they want to go off and do. Or some might fear they don't have the financial resources to get started, and for a lot of people, it's just the plain fear of failure, and wondering what their families and friends are going to think. But the bottom line is, if they don't take that first step, they'll never clearly know and understand the feeling of accomplishment, the exhilaration of success. And that starts with figuring out what your passion is. Which it sounds like you have. So now align that with your talents, and then identify the right path to take. And take on the attitude of never quitting, which is the most common cause for failure with most businesses. Often times, successful people, despite the adversities they encounter, are able to find a way to get through and to ultimately succeed. Going through that process and those setbacks is where they can not only overcome them but find greater opportunities or benefits that they may be able to pursue as a result of going through those setbacks."

"That's a good way of looking at it," Hannah said. "I guess it's just a matter of reminding myself that these things will ultimately provide some learning experience. Sometimes it's hard to do that when you're right in the middle of it. Like when I'm sitting there trying to write this mission statement and the only thing I seem to be able to come up with is jibberish."

"But it was there all along. You just had to clear some of the other stuff out of the way to get to it. You've got to stay focused and targeted, and a great way to do this is to set goals. Write them down. Have a clear plan. Review your plan on a daily basis. This will help keep you focused and moving forward. It's especially critical to have short-term goals, small steps that will have you moving forward. If you see yourself making progress—however small—you'll be rewarding yourself through the process that will ultimately get you to the mid- and long-term goals that you're trying to accomplish. And don't be afraid to seek counsel from others that have already done what you want to do and what you want to accomplish. Learn from their successes as well as their mistakes. Having your own business allows you so much more freedom and control over your own life as far as what you can do as a result of that."

"I like the idea of small-term goals. That was one of the things that would seem to paralyze me—thinking about the big picture. I'm not saying I don't think it's important to think about that, but sometimes it just seems so overwhelming and like I don't have even the slightest clue where to begin. But short-term goals are good. I need to keep reminding myself to set manageable tasks."

"It's one of the best ways to let yourself see the progress you're making," Lynn said. He looked down at the book in front of him. "Clearly, you had success as a literary agent, so I'm sure you'll find success in your new endeavors, as well."

"I hope I will," Hannah said. "Thank you for the great advice."

Later that evening, she typed up an official version of her mission statement, and checked the short-term goal off her list.

Chapter 17

PEOPLE, PURPOSE, PASSION

Hannah continued to make lists. She stood in front of the mirror each morning, sometimes for sixty seconds, sometimes a little longer, and told herself she was capable, could handle this, would succeed. She was surprised at how willing her family and friends were to provide donations, and she began looking for a suitable space to rent. She started reaching out to people in the area she might be able to work with: counselors, therapists, even a woman who did Reiki and aromatherapy had expressed interest in offering her services. Hannah called one of her former assistants, whose mother was a nurse at Lenox Hill. She made a lunch date with the girl's mother, Abbey, and the two women spent the better part of the afternoon discussing the ways in which the organization could be beneficial.

"I also want to pass along the contact info for a co-worker's daughter," Abbey said. "Her name is Celeste and she just graduated from Eugene Lang. She's thinking about going to graduate school, but I know she's also looking for things to get involved in, and she's very interested in nonprofit work. You should give her a call."

"I will," Hannah said. "Thanks for the tip."

She called Celeste later that evening and was pleased that they hit it off right away.

"This sounds like a great organization," she said. "I've been talking with some people from a few other organizations—more nature and environment related stuff—but this would be right up my alley. I had a friend growing up who fell off her horse once and had lasting effects from the injury. It wasn't like she had to stay in the hospital overnight or anything, but things were different for her after. I never said anything, but I think, actually, maybe part of the reason why things were like that for her was because she didn't get a correct diagnosis right away. It seems that with people who suffer mild head injuries, if there aren't huge red flags, then they usually don't take the right precautions, which can end up hurting them in the long run."

"You sound exactly like the person I'd like to work with," Hannah said.

They talked for a while longer, and by the time the conversation ended, they decided to hold a support group, in exactly one month, which Hannah hoped would bring people together and give them the opportunity to let her know about their needs. If she hadn't found a place to rent by then, she'd have it in her apartment.

On Tuesday, she went to Brooklyn to look at a potential rental in the Windsor Terrace neighborhood, near Prospect Park and the subway station. It was on the ground level, with a large main room and two smaller rooms toward the back. It had been previously used as a massage therapy office, and there was still a faint scent of lavender and some other essential oil lingering in the air.

She left with the rental application and walked to a nearby café to fill it out. She ordered tea and sat at the counter atop a high stool. When she finished filling out the application, she swiveled around on the stool and looked at the other patrons in the café. She needed to find at least two other people who could serve on the board of directors with her. She'd posted an ad on Craigslist and had received a number of responses that she planned to go through later today, though she felt somewhat uncertain about how she'd choose the right people. She hoped it would just be a feeling that came over her; when she came into contact with the right people, she'd know. This wasn't like publishing where she knew all the ins and outs, had numerous contacts, and had been in the business for years.

She turned back to the counter and doodled a little on her notepad. She wasn't ready to go back outside and face the cold wind yet. The entrance to the subway station wasn't far but she needed to go drop the rental application off first, and that would be a bit of a walk. She got a refill on her tea and started talking with the woman who was sitting next to her. The woman's name was Sandy Crow, and she had also recently started a company.

"Do you have any helpful tips?" Hannah asked. "I've felt really fortunate since I decided to do this whole thing—I've met some really great people who have given me some invaluable advice. It really is kind of amazing, the way the universe will provide you with what you need at just the right time."

"It is, isn't it?" Sandy said. "I was actually inspired to start my business from a dream of seeing businesses and their employees form a stronger collaboration. Many employees segment their work lives rather than integrate them. If I could offer you some advice … I think the most important thing to remember is that employees should always come first. Take my company, for example. The slogan is: People, Purpose, and Passion Matter. And really, if we're to be honest, that's the heart and soul of every company. Hannah, you have the opportunity to really make a difference, not just in the lives that your organization is helping, but you can inspire your employees to be creative, passionate and purposeful by ensuring they feel valued and that their contribution is important to your organization. They in turn share that appreciation and inspiration and apply it to the workplace, customer relations, family units, and various community volunteer opportunities. It's a domino effect. It shows that we're all connected and touch each other's lives in more ways than we imagine."

"I never thought of it like a domino effect, but you're right."

"To really inspire and encourage others, help them see their greatness; be a mentor. Practice the art of giving. It's really the key to feeling connected and supported. So ask for help or advice from a mentor or someone who can help you see through the trees that may be blocking your vision. Be a giver. Ask yourself, 'How can I be of service and make other people feel like they matter?' By helping other people feel like they matter, it will in turn help you feel valued. It is said, 'Teachers actually learn more from their students.'"

Hannah picked up her teacup and blew on the steam. She'd always felt fortunate in the jobs she'd had, that her bosses were amicable, respectful, and treated her well. Whether her own organization stayed small or grew to employ many people, she made the resolution right then and there to always make sure they knew they were appreciated.

"It really does make such a difference," she said. "For any job. I guess all anyone really wants is to know that what they're doing means something to someone and that they are valued."

"Exactly," Sandy said. "Something I like to do each morning is start off by thinking of three people I'm grateful for. Be a cheerleader for others and acknowledge people that I work with or come into contact with, which can be a simple 'Hello' or 'Thank you'. Ask yourself, 'What is it that makes my life worthwhile? What do I want to be in the world?'

And that goes hand in hand with what makes you smile and what do you love doing."

"You're absolutely right," Hannah said. "And that totally encompasses your business's slogan."

"Exactly. Those things matter. And if you're going to be someone's boss, you really have the power to transform your employees' lives by truly engaging them in what they do. A boss needs to notice how they impact or can impact their employees just by their words and attitude. One kind word can change someone's life. When you think about how much time people spend at work, it seems crazy to think that bosses would do anything but try to engage their employees and help them reach their fullest potential. As a mentor, a boss should be mentoring an employee to receive an 'A' and showcase their skills and talents."

"It really does make a difference," Hannah said. "I remember my first job was dishwashing at this little restaurant in Sonoma, and the owner was also the head chef and he was just so miserable all the time. And yeah, I was just a lowly dishwasher, and it was just a summer job, but the entire wait staff was miserable, all the other chefs were miserable, even though it was this really fancy, four-star place. And then the next summer I ended up working at an ice cream shop, and the boss there had such a different attitude. Maybe there wasn't as much pressure or something, but my boss at the ice cream place was always smiling, not just at the customers, but at the staff, too, and wasn't afraid to let people know that he appreciated their hard work. And it was hard—maybe just as hard as dishwashing—but it felt like it was easier to do because the boss appreciated what we were doing."

"It's amazing how big of a difference it makes, isn't it?" Sandy said.

Hannah nodded. "Yeah. And so of course, I want to be like that, too. I want the people I work with to feel inspired by me and engaged. I'm still really in the beginning stages of this. I mean, things are definitely moving along—I just filled out a rental application for office space, actually—but I feel like I have a long way to go."

"Let me give you the name of this guy I'm working with," Sandy said, reaching for her purse. "He's been helping me brand and market my company so I can consult businesses and employees to excel; you might want to talk with him. His name is Wes Chapman and he's great. Really good at helping you see the bigger picture on things."

After she finished her tea and said goodbye to Sandy, Hannah zipped up her jacket and went to drop the rental application off before heading back to the city, where she'd spend the rest of the day going through the responses she received on Craigslist.

Chapter 18

INNOVATIVE SPIRIT

After a week of going through resumes and cover letters, Hannah called Conner and asked for help.

"I can't decide. Everyone sounds good," she said. "They're all passionate and hard-working. And some of them have relatives or friends that have suffered from head injuries. How am I supposed to choose? Can I read you some?"

"Please!" Conner said. "I'm good at making decisions like this. But first, Han, tell me how it's going."

She smiled. "Okay."

They talked for a little while and then she started reading him some of the cover letters. "I only need to find one more board member," she said. "We need three, and I've already got one, that girl whose mom is a nurse. Her name's Celeste, and she's so enthusiastic and eager, and she's really smart, too, so it's kind of perfect."

"All these people sound pretty good," Conner admitted.

"I know. But there's way too many for me to interview all of them. I'd spend the next three months just doing that."

"Maybe just close your eyes and pick five from the pile and call those people in for interviews? Sorry I can't offer a more scientific method for choosing."

After Hannah hung up with Conner, she sat with the phone in her lap for a moment. She reached for her purse and dug around until she found the slip of paper Sandy had written Wes Chapman's phone number on. She dialed it without thinking of what she'd actually say if he picked up, and when he answered, she stuttered.

"I'm sorry," she said, clearing her throat a few times. "My name's Hannah Braun. I happened to run into Sandy Crow recently and she gave me your number."

"Sandy, sure," Wes said. "We've been working together. How are you, Hannah?"

"Um, I'm okay. I'm actually not entirely sure why I'm calling, other than I'm starting this nonprofit, and Sandy mentioned that you're really good at seeing the bigger picture on things, and you're helping her with her new company ..." Hannah trailed off. If she had a question, she wasn't exactly sure what it was.

"Is there something in particular you're having trouble with at the moment?"

"Well ... actually, yes. I'm trying to find at least one other person to be on the board of directors for my nonprofit. I posted on Craigslist and received a lot of great responses. Pretty much everyone sounds like they'd be a good fit. I know this is just the first step in finding people to work with, but it just seems like it's going to be really hard to make a decision."

"That makes me happy to hear there are so many eager people out there that responded to your listing," Wes said. "That's the one thing that I think would help this world more than anything else: if everyone really understood work ethic."

Hannah considered this. "That makes a lot of sense," she said. "It might not solve all problems, but it would solve a lot of them."

"If we all understood what it takes to make a great universe and a great planet," Wes continued, "I think we'd respect each other a lot more and there'd be more love, more joy, and a lot less poverty. It's something that has made countries great and powerful and then it seems once they get to that great and powerful status they begin to really lose the foresight of what got them to that level. And they start becoming lazy and self-entitled, and then we start this cycle all over again. I wish that people could maintain the work ethic that it takes to become great because through greatness we can achieve anything. I think we put too much status into becoming great; we already are! We just have to use that greatness to achieve. So you've kind of got a good problem. You've got an abundance of people who sound like they'd be really eager and excited to work with you."

Hannah laughed. "Yes, when you put it that way, I guess it doesn't sound so bad."

"Usually when people are stuck or discouraged, it's because they can't see past their own hand. Think of it like a horse with blinders on. You spend so much time and energy on this project of yours that sometimes it takes an outside person to be able to see the solutions."

"Well, you're an outside person. What do you think I should do?"

"What are the qualities your ideal candidate would have?"

"Honestly? My ideal candidate for this would be my friend, Conner. He's actually part of the reason why I started this whole thing to begin with. He's caring, kind, he's got the sort of personality people gravitate to, and he's got personal experience with what this nonprofit is all about."

"Well … if he's your ideal candidate, why not bring him on board?"

"Because I can't—" Hannah stopped short. Could she? Was it required that a board member live in the same state? If it wasn't, then she would call Conner the second she got off the phone and ask him to be the third member. "You're totally right," she said. "That's my answer. Thank you so much."

"You're very welcome! I'm glad I could be helpful. Let me tell you one more thing, though, to keep in mind. Three things, actually. You've got to be passionate, you've got to have work ethic, and you've got to be able to adapt. What you think is a good idea one day might not be next week.

Or maybe something has changed or a new opportunity has come up. You've got to be fluid, and your business has to be fluid enough that you can move in different directions and kind of sway with the wind, much like a tree."

"That's a good image. The tree bending but not breaking."

"It really is. I wish you the best of luck with this, Hannah."

"Thanks so much, Wes. I really appreciate you taking the time to talk with me."

She hung up the phone and dialed Conner's number.

"Hello?" he answered.

"Hi there," she said. "I'd like to offer you a job."

Chapter 19

BRILLIANCE

Spring seemed to arrive early, and there was a week in late March when the temperatures topped out in the low seventies. Hannah felt lifted, vibrant, as though this was a nod from Mother Nature herself that everything was going exactly as it should.

Better Beginnings was hosting an open house later that afternoon, and a community dinner at Lucia's that weekend. Though there'd already been several informal support groups and meetings, Hannah decided to have the open house serve as the grand opening, so she bought flowers and put up an orange ribbon—Conner's favorite color—to be cut. She stepped outside, wedging a doorstop under the door. Next to the door hung the sign, a sans serif font engraved on birdseye maple. It was simple but effective, exactly what she hoped her organization would be. She stepped back and looked at it. The sun was warm on the top of her head and she couldn't help but smile at the sign, the embodiment of everything she'd been working toward.

A man was walking by. She caught his eye as she stepped out of his way and smiled. "Hi," she said.

"Hello," he replied. He stopped next to her and looked into the open door. "What is this place?"

"We're a new nonprofit. Better Beginnings. We provide resources and respite for people who have suffered from traumatic brain injuries. Today is our grand opening. And we're having a fundraiser dinner this weekend, at Lucia's."

"They make a great seafood scaloppini there," the man said. He held his hand out. "I'm Carl Sheeler."

"Hannah Braun."

He smiled at her. "You've got that sparkle in your eye, Hannah. I like to see that."

She looked at him more closely, not entirely sure what he meant. "Do I?"

"You do. I hope you never lose it. It reminds me of this phrase of mine; can I share it with you?"

"Of course," Hannah said.

"I enjoy phrases that are double, if not triple, entendres. One of my favorites is: 'The difference between being bright and being brilliant is the amount of energy brought forth.' The point of that phrase is that most of us have good ideas in our minds, and some of them are pretty darn intelligent. But absent of energy, brilliance won't come. There's a lot of impoverished geniuses. And you've got to wonder why that is. I think it's the degree of positive and selfless energy. As more energy goes into something that's bright, it becomes brilliant. And, as more energy goes into deeper understanding, one becomes wiser, also known as brilliance. And then also, energy can be defined in two ways: the energy like electricity or our physical manifestation of energy, which allows us to go from having knowledge to bringing knowledge to bear to make positive change."

"It has taken a lot of energy to get this place going," Hannah agreed. "But it was all worth it. And I know it's going to take even more energy to *keep* it going, but I'm ready for that challenge. I've got a good support system."

"That's good. I think a lot of people underestimate the importance of a good support system. Many of us start out life with the belief the playing field will be level and the more I apply myself the more elevated I will become. But something often happens within twenty years from the time we're on our own—we find we and many of our dreams have been ground down by the fact that merit and sacrifice is not always rewarded. We've got to pay our expenses and make sure that our kid's braces are taken care of and our boss is happy as is our significant other. It becomes life not as imagined but as it is. So some people one day suddenly realize that they were bright when they started, but the brilliance has dimmed somewhat. Where is the spark? It's when you enable others to become successful. Your success comes as a byproduct of your faith in others. The simple term is 'giver's gain'. When the market crashed in 2008, many local professionals began to panic and turned inward.

It was my opportunity to create STAR (Strategic Trusted Advisors Roundtable) in order to connect professionals at local gatherings where they are challenged to help each other first. It created thousands of new relationships; millions in commerce and hundreds of thousands in philanthropy. Many people embrace the concept of fostering transformative relationships, but very few are willing to put sufficient energy into it. They default to 'one and done' transactions over people-centered relationships. But I think you have the energy to transform. You understand what someone's about; you help them achieve their goals; and then, as a byproduct of helping enough people, it comes back to you. It's karmic. And what you're doing, Hannah, you're helping people. And it will come back one-hundred-fold."

She smiled as she thought about all the people who had been so generous with their advice, she thought of Conner's expression when she told him how the opening went. "It already has," she said.

From the Brooklyn Daily Eagle

Better Beginnings will commemorate its fifth anniversary later this month by publishing a memoir entitled *Blooming,* by Victor Harwood. Mr. Harwood suffered a traumatic brain injury several years ago and has been involved with Better Beginnings since its inception.

It is familiar territory for its founder, Hannah Braun, who left a successful career in publishing to begin the organization. Since opening, Better Beginnings has helped hundreds of people who have been affected by traumatic brain injuries live fuller, more independent lives. The center offers weekly classes and support groups and has a number of skilled occupational and physical therapists on its staff. The center also provides funds for those in need; please speak to an intake counselor for more information. A number of fun events are held each year, including the Better Beginnings 5K and 10K, and several community meals hosted at various restaurants. The center also celebrated the opening of its sister office in Boston last year. Work for the Better Beginnings Home, an assisted-living facility for adults living with traumatic brain injury and acquired brain injury, is slated to begin next month at the former Wentworth Estate, which Eileen Wentworth had bequeathed to the center.

Rounding out what has been a very busy and fulfilling past year, the center is pleased to announce that Ms. Braun will be marrying her longtime friend and partner, Conner Tero, one of the original board members, and one of the two people Hannah credits with having inspired her to begin the center in the first place.

Co-Author Biographies

Bradley Alt

Bradley started out working as a trash man in San Diego, but with a burning desire to help people, he became a firefighter/paramedic. Still not completely satisfied, wanting to change people's lives before they got sick or in to an accident, he started a personal interactive entertainment company. As he developed the company, he immersed himself into the personal development field and found his true calling of serving the world. Now, Bradley is a personal development coach and corporate team building specialist, as well as an enthusiastic professional speaker. He spends his off time with his beautiful wife and his three children in San Diego, CA.

Bradley can be reached at (888) 909-2792 or info@BradleyTAlt.com or BradleyTAlt.com.

Christine Alt

A native to San Diego, CA, Christine is an entrepreneur, professional speaker, personal development coach, corporate team building trainer, model, loving wife and mother of three, which has given her the greatest fulfillment in life. She was taught that through persistence, love and happiness, anything is possible and you can live an extraordinary life. She dedicates this to her "Angel" grandmother Virginia Emma Valdivia Velez for taking the journey and challenge to let us know that dreams are possible! To many more fun times, great memories, adventures and surprises.

For more information, visit: www.felizgoddess.com or you can reach Christine at christine@felizgoddess.com.

Lynn Barnes, Jr.

Lynn Barnes has an insatiable thirst for challenge and adventure, a never ending enthusiasm and zest for life, a perpetual desire for growth, an investment in life-long learning, a deep, heart-felt thankfulness to his creator for his many blessings and a commitment that goes beyond the old standard of customer satisfaction to a new standard of personal client care. These qualities and having a motto of "Never quit! Never give up!" are just some of the driving forces behind Lynn's immense success as a business entrepreneur, real estate investor and mentor, software developer, author and multi-company CEO and owner.

Lynn has over 28 years of global, high-technology customer relations experience, representing and supporting premier Fortune 100 corporations in areas ranging from global manufacturing, customer quality and service, sales and marketing support, software development and implementation, supply chain and logistics, consumer products integration and high-tech storage solutions.

Before beginning his real estate entrepreneurship in 2002, Lynn held multi-faceted positions focused on providing global clients with a superior customer experience and cutting-edge technical support. These experiences allowed him to polish his skills in listening and problem solving—both of which give his clients a decided advantage and have allowed him to become known by many as the "Troubleshooter": one that quickly goes in, analyzes a challenging situation, identifies the root cause, and defines a clear and concise action plan from the most beneficial, cost effective solution, then implements that solution with identified controls to prevent the challenge from reoccurrence.

After servicing his country in the U.S. Air Force from 1977 to 1983 in the 349th Military Air Command (MAC) as a Sr. Staff Sargent, Lynn began his career in the high-technology industry working for a small start-up company, Lassen Electronics. There he quickly accelerated in both his learning and position, while overseeing the manufacturing assembly group responsible for manufacturing major electronic sub-assemblies used by high-tech companies all across the country. Lynn went on to work for many other high-tech companies in the San Francisco Bay area and specifically Silicon Valley.

Early on in his high-technology career in 1982, Lynn started his first start-up business, Selket, where he developed, manufactured and sold one of the first specialized surface metrology test equipment used in the high-tech storage media industry. It was the first use of fiber optical profile to employ coherence scanning interferometry, also known as white-light interferometry, white-light confocal, or vertical scanning interferometry to produce high quality two-dimensional surface maps of the object under test. This equipment measured and statistically analyzed the topography of aluminum, ceramic and glass platters that hard disc drive (HDD) manufacturers use, as a medium by which a computer electronically stores information. Lynn was highly successful at the international marketing of this specialized test equipment for what was then a fast growing high-tech storage disc drive industry.

As the high-tech storage industry began to shrink due to market pressures, overseas competition and increasing prices, Lynn went on to work for many high-technology companies between 1983 and 1985 in the PC and consumer electronics storage solutions market, including but not limited to companies like Atari, Osborne Computers, Fairchild Semiconductor and Western Digital Corporation.

In 1985 Lynn began his career at Conner Peripherals in Longmont, Colorado as a customer field applications engineer providing technical support to major client OEM accounts. In 1996, after the acquisition of Conner

Peripherals by Seagate Technology, he held the position of a senior certified Six Sigma Black Belt in statistics and global customer technical support account manager. In that role, Lynn provided multi-billion dollar companies such as Apple, Dell, HP and Microsoft, to name a few, with strategic and tactical technical support while he led Six Sigma centric teams through the analytical process of identifying areas within their business processes where cost-savings efforts could be taken, and developing and implementing an action plan to bring that cost-savings to realization. Lynn's unique expertise lies with cultivating key relationships and bringing a team to the realization of any goal they set before themselves.

Lynn founded his first real estate business in 2002, J & L Realty, LLC, where he began investing in the single family residence (SFR), duplexes and four-plex properties throughout the mid-west and south-east areas of the country for passive income. After the devastating results that Hurricane Katrina, one of the deadliest and most destructive hurricanes ever recorded in U.S. history, had on New Orleans and the surrounding Gulf Coast region, Lynn jumped into action to help lead a group of real estate investors provide new homes for those left homeless, and helped over fifty families find a place they could call home. In 2010, Lynn began investing in commercial multi-family properties of twenty-plus units with the goal of "bringing back our neighborhoods, one home at a time" and has been quite successful at helping others find a good, safe place they can call home.

In 2012, along with managing his other multi-company real estate businesses, Lynn founded and became the CEO and owner of J & L Infinite Investments, LLC, a company that buys both residential and commercial defaulted, non-performing mortgage notes from all across the country through local regional banks and large hedge funds for his own portfolio. The primary goal is to provide a win-win-win solution to the country's devastating market crash of 2007/2008. Lynn accomplished this by 1) helping banks to remove "bad" debt from their financial books and allowing them to remain solvent, within federal banking requirements and able to lend more money out to the public consumer to further stimulate the economic and business growth of the country, 2) helping property owners that for whatever reason, such as a job loss or a major family illness, have found themselves unable to make their monthly mortgage payments, have an opportunity for multiple recovery strategies that most banks are not in a position to facilitate and begin rebuilding their lives and financial credit and 3) teaching others that have no time and no means to earn a good rate of return on cash they have sitting in a bank or IRA account that is otherwise earning little to no interest, on how they can earn a good rate of return.

Lynn lives in the San Francisco Bay area with his lovely wife Jun and their seven-year-old daughter, Angelina and has two adult children, Joshua and Michelle, both living in the Ohio area with their own families. Lynn describes himself as a happy and fortunate person, and he brings that positive attitude to everything he undertakes. Patience is a rare quality in today's hurry-up world and a gift that Lynn gives freely, along with time and detailed attention—listening while his clients share their dreams, goals and aspirations, then answering their questions and helping them explore their options for financial wealth and freedom. To learn more about Lynn and the exciting opportunities available in the real estate market today, contact him at www.DistressedNoteSolutions.com, www.DistressedAssetDoctors.com, at http://www.linkedin.com/pub/lynn-barnes-jr/10/550/2b5/ or you may call Lynn at (408) 647-1115.

Wes Chapman

Wes is known as the "Five Star Guy," and is a dream making, wish granting, business visionary. He knows that your success is just around the corner.

Five Star means something to everyone, but globally it is defined as the best, the highest plateau, the greatest accomplishment and the highest quality. Wes Chapman is the Five Star Guy and he will show you how you can achieve ultimate success in life, and the work place and in your business. Join him as he will guide you to your Five Star lifestyle. He will help you look ahead and show you how you can see tomorrow's opportunities today.

With over twenty-one years of experience in marketing, design, creative, advertising and business-to-business sales, Wes has had the opportunity to work with some of the greatest minds to walk the planet. From Bill Gates to Greg S. Reid. He has worked with over 353 different types of businesses, including those in the entertainment world, services, and retail. Wesley has experienced four technological revolutions: computers, the web, cell phones, and most recently, interactive user technology.

He is a tech-savvy, computer loving, sport playing guy! Loves football, basketball and soccer. He watches football like it was a gospel and follows Real Salt Lake and Minnesota Vikings 'til the end.

He falls under the classification of a self-made man even though without the support he has had around him he could not be who he is today. To learn more about Wes, visit www.fivestarguy.com.

Sandy Crow

As a corporate finance leader, Sandy Crow has spent more than twenty years working with leaders to strategically improve financial results by identifying business drivers, establishing KPI's, setting in place revenue and cash accelerators, and developing cost saving strategies. Throughout her financial career, Sandy has had the good fortune to work for some of the best leaders who have transformed companies into great-performing companies.

Sandy believes the most important business driver is a company's workforce and the managing of the workforce. Leveraging an excellent leadership team is the key to transforming employees into committed top performers.

As the founder of Gencon, a leadership training and consulting firm, Sandy helps companies build a "new workforce" centered on people, purpose and passion. A workforce committed to top performance, integrating and aligning personal and work goals, and generational connectivity. Gencon has programs developed to create a "new workforce" positioned to collaborate with company leaders in building an empowered company culture to achieving company goals.

To learn more visit www.genconinc.com or connect with Sandy at sandy@genconinc.com or (858) 775-0829.

Scott Duffy

Scott Duffy is a high-energy entrepreneur and business growth expert. He began his career working for best-selling author and speaker, Tony Robbins, and went on to help launch small businesses that became big brands like CBS Sportsline, NBC Internet, and FOXSports.com. Next, he founded Smart Charter, an online booking tool for private aviation, which was acquired by Richard Branson's Virgin Group. Scott is a passionate advocate for entrepreneurship and has been a guest in numerous media outlets including CNBC, FOX News, *The Wall Street Journal*, and *Business Week*. Scott's book, *LAUNCH!*, from Penguin Publishing, is a blueprint for business leaders to launch new businesses, products, and services. Scott currently lives in Southern California with his wife and two children. You can reach him at connect@scottduffy.com or visit his website at www.scottduffy.com.

Camden Garcia

Camden Brent Garcia was born in 1996. When he was five, he had a brain tumor, and at ten he had a compressed skull fracture. He's currently doing well and feels God has a plan for him, so he uses his testimony to give God the glory! He started a cross ministry when he was six where every Sunday he gives a cross away. He builds crosses that are all over the world. Make-a-Wish is a big part of his life.

They granted him a wish and now he gets to raise money to help other kids fulfill their wishes. Camden speaks to various organizations and schools; his first was when he was nine at the Make-a-Wish National Reception.

Now, ten years cancer free, Camden wrestles varsity and runs cross country for his high school. He is a member of the Fellowship of Christian Athletes and is on the Teen Advisory Council Board at the University Medical Center Hospital.

His favorite hobby is restoring an old 53 Ford pick-up that he took completely apart when I was just six.

Camden feels blessed to be able to help others and give hope. You find more information at www.CamdensCrosses.com.

Yvan S. Gosselin

From an early age, Yvan S. Gosselin, PhD. was destined for uncommon professional achievement. He climbed the ladder of success by adopting a very positive attitude, finding confidence and enthusiasm to be the essential tools of a future winner. Through hard lessons engendered in adversity, he has also learned to take the necessary distance in order to rebound when faced with the seemingly insurmountable. Holder of a Ph.D. from the University of Montreal and Bonn in Germany, the co-author has taught for twenty years at universities in Canada, displaying a fundamental desire for constant learning, and sharing that learning with his students in such a way as to instill in them a taste for success derived from principles of constant self improvement. He now devotes a second career in business to bringing his wealth of experience to bear in advising and counseling captains of industry with winning strategies. Having completed a world tour, during which he had the immense opportunity to meet business people of many different cultures, he is focusing his current efforts on writing books about success and wealth. With the knowledge and varied experience he has garnered over the years, he gives generously of his time to advise people on finding the path to success and enthusiasm in their daily lives. He is in this respect a strong advocate of the principles of success taught by illustrious authors such as Dr. Napoleon Hill and Dr. Norman Vincent Peale.

He can be reached at segei11@videotron.ca.

Jote Kaur

Inspired transformational thought leader, TRUISO founder, and visionary entrepreneur.

Jote is the CEO and founder of TRUISO. She created TRUISO and its philosophy for the purpose of becoming a global megabrand to help business- and pleasure travelers, who struggle with their health on and off the road, as well as those who want to live a balanced life.

Jote's mission is to share the gift of health, power, happiness, love and joy with millions of people on the planet, one person, one life, one soul at a time—as she believes that every soul in the universe deserves to be encompassed in strength. She created TRUISO to be a multi-sensory, holistic conglomerate of unique products, educational experiences, instructional videos and design services that will help people transform their health, self-esteem, environment and life.

Jote is a passionate life designer, who brilliantly creates harmonious stress-free environments. She is passionate about holistic, luxurious, organic, sensual living; she loves luxurious, healthy travel experiences; she is a walking and living example of delicious yet nutritious eating. As a master yogini, she is the creator of her own yoga brand YogaJote. She not only deeply understands the mind-body-spirit connection; she lives it every single day.

She is an out-of-the-box thinker with a determined attitude and more than two decades of experience in the arts, fitness and nutrition. As a young person, she developed a passion for nutritious and healthy eating and later became a certified personal trainer in 2003. She has also been a member of the Yoga Alliance as an instructor since 2007, and in 2008, she was certified as a pilates instructor by the Physical Mind Institute.

Her one-hundred-percent focus is the application of her passion in life: Love, Sensuality, Health, Music, Design, Spirituality and Environmentalism.

She is determined to collaborate with heart-centered, environmentally responsible developers, hotel owners, business owners, and individual clients, who will benefit from the harmonizing, healing, balancing effect of incorporating the TRUISO way into their lives and spaces. Visit www.truiso.com for more information. You can also reach Jote at yogajote@gmail.com or (305) 915-6811.

Rick Kvalheim

Rick Kvalheim is an entrepreneur that embodies the adage, "one man's trash is another man's treasure." For nearly twenty years Rick worked in the aluminum recycling industry processing scrap from aerospace, automotive, industrial, military, and consumer waste streams. The material was smelted and alloyed to specification, then made into aluminum ingots and shipped from coast to coast as well as exported to Japan, Mexico, Taiwan and a few other countries.

In recent years Rick has turned his attention to recycling houses. By buying houses that are too damaged to qualify for any type of conventional financing and renovating them, the damaged property can be turned into "the nicest house on the block". Not only does Rick find this creatively satisfying, but enjoys being able to offer local jobs in this economy.

Rick is also the president of a California nonprofit, Warriors Way to Wealth. The mission is to encourage and assist the men and women who provide extraordinary services to our great nation, build wealth, stability, independence and financial security. Warriors Way to Wealth is dedicated to provide programs that empower those individuals who protect, serve and defend our country. To provide choices and opportunities that foster financial responsibility, accountability, homeownership, wealth creation and entrepreneurship. Visit Rick's websites www.papabuyshomes.com and www.fhsinvesting.com for more information. You can contact Rick by email at rickkvalheim@kvalheim.us or (760) 792-0050.

Joan Magill

Joan Magill is a successful female entrepreneur of for-profit and nonprofit companies. She is recognized for running one of the fifty largest women-owned businesses in Baltimore by net revenue. Among her many recognitions, she was awarded Women of the Year by a national nonprofit organization, and was the first women to receive, Associate of the Year, the highest award an associate can receive, by a national trade association. She is known as a visionary, creating and building niche businesses from start-up, filling avoids in the marketplace, both regionally and nationally. She is an educator, a certified team-building coach, and curriculum creator.

At the start of her career, she persevered through difficult circumstances, having experienced being the only women serving in leadership positions on various professional association councils and boards of directors. Her leadership quickly earned the respect of her peers with her uncompromising work ethic and proven record of success. Being top in her industry, she is a national consultant and expert witness for high-profile cases. She is an active volunteer board member for several organizations in her community, and has served as a past trustee on the leadership council of her temple. She is passionate about empowering and creating sustainable entrepreneurship opportunities for women, in the workforce, asset building for all children especially the underpriviledged, and devoted to a sustainable cleaner greener environment through corporate and social responsibility. Joan can be contacted at joan@joanmagill.com and (410) 340-9196.

Dave Michal

Dave Michal, principal and co-partner of Like-Minded Entrepreneurs, LLC, has over twenty-five years of experience in real estate acquisition and disposition, investment analysis and management, residential and commercial real estate, building construction and land development, building repairs, tenant improvements, construction cost estimating, property casualty consulting, specialized property decontamination and remediation, company structuring and funding, and self-directed IRA and 401K investing. All combined, his past and present businesses and contractual relationships have conducted business in the nine-figure range. These businesses have developed, built, purchased, and consulted in real estate projects, property loss, and property investments of all types, Dave offers a perspective that few others are able to provide when it comes to these types of businesses.

From his beginnings through today, Dave learned that being an entrepreneur sounded great as a kid, but to choose entrepreneurship as a career path would mean embracing the willingness to step up to unexpected challenges and hardships. All business owners at some point experience this fight to succeed in order to receive the final reward of financial freedom. Dave would not have it any other way, dealing with the challenges and seeing your endeavors reach success is where you feel the highest level of financial rewards and blessings. Dave believes these business experiences are the blessings God has put in front of him and good or bad they all open the next door to growth in his business and investing career. Visit www.davemichal.com to learn more.

Jason Munson

Jason Munson is a leader in the fight against high home heating cost in the bio-fuel industry. He has built an international selling platform that assists his clients with their home heating needs quickly and at low cost. His current focus is to become the Bob Vila of the home heating industry in the pellet stove category. Jason believes in providing an excellent service in an awesome way, working very hard to support his clients and enjoying the rewards.

Jason has achieved the dream of being able to run his business from any beach in the world where he has a cell-phone signal. An avid kiteboarder you can often find Jason working from his mobile office or wherever there is a nice beach with a good wind; talking on the phone one minute and then flying across the water the next. He finds the freedom of entrepreneurship exhilarating as he travels with his family to exotic locations. www.pelletstovepro.com

Tim Murphy

Tim has worked for many great entrepreneurs and franchise owners during his career. During Tim's franchise career, he had the fortunate opportunity to work for the central Florida Applebee's as CFO and be mentored by Abe Gustin, Jr., the former chairman and CEO of Applebee's International after retiring from Applebee's. Abe showed Tim how to properly grow a concept, develop good franchisee relationships and what matters most in creating wealth through franchising. The time spent with Abe Gustin, Jr. and the lessons learned … were priceless.

Tim has over thirty years in C-level and senior level franchise and hospitality management experience with public, private and start-up companies. Tim is currently the president of Advanced Franchise Systems Inc. and chief executive officer and founder of PHresh Kitchen Inc. Advanced Franchise Systems, coaches and advises companies and individuals how to create wealth through franchising their companies and concepts with speed, reduced costs and integrity. "Do you or someone you know have a company that needs help franchising their concept or idea, or an existing franchise concept that just needs coaching to get to the next level?" Tim created a franchise coaching system to advise franchise clients how to properly, quickly, and with reduced cost, franchise their businesses. So if you, or someone you know, could use franchise coaching advice, please contact Tim.

PHresh Kitchen is a modular fast-casual food and beverage franchise company that capitalizes on the consumer trend to eat low-calorie and healthful foods in high-foot traffic locations. "Do you or someone you know have a hard time finding low-calorie and healthful foods when and where you want it?" Tim has created a modular fast-casual franchise concept with low-calorie healthful food options that are placed in high-foot traffic locations like hospitals, universities, airports and big box retail areas. If you would like to participate, want to become a future franchisee, or want to learn more, please contact Tim.

Tim was the CEO and co-founder of Zealthy (a precursor for PHresh Kitchen), CFO for Sonny's Real Pit Bar-B-Q and CFO at Applebee's franchisee in Orlando (also owner of Green Hills Grilles and investment in Ray's on the River in Atlanta). Tim has worked for Darden Restaurants (Olive Garden, Red Lobster, Bahama Breeze and China Coast), Advantica Restaurants (Denny's, Hardee's, El Pollo Loco, Coco's, Carrows, Quincy's, Winchell Donuts, Mother Butler Pies, Volume Services and Canteen Services), Walt Disney World in Orlando, Florida, consulted for companies as CFO and has developed multiple commercial properties including restaurants, retail, office space, golf resorts and planned communities. Tim is a licensed commercial real estate broker in the State of Florida and a lifetime member of CEO Space International.

Tim has a strong commitment to the community and serves as co-chairperson for the JDRF Walk (Juvenile Diabetes Research Foundation) held annually at the University of Central Florida. Tim has also served as scoutmaster and chairperson for Boy Scout Troop 58 in Oviedo, Florida, and served as assistant treasurer on the eighth largest Boy Scout council in the United States. Tim is an Eagle Scout, and highly values honest- and integrity filled professional and personal relationships.

Tim's personal passion is running long distances and staying healthy. Tim has run several races (5K's, 10K's, half and full marathons including four Walt Disney World Marathons and the New York City Marathon, two Disney Goofy Challenges—39.3 miles in two days, and signed up for the initial 2014 Disney Dopey Challenge—48.6 miles—on behalf of JDRF and his son Troy, who is type-1 diabetic). Tim is now shifting his running focus and setting sights on creating the Run 2 End Obesity nonprofit to aid in reducing or eliminating obesity through education and teaching adults and children how to eat less and move more, through the workplace and schools. Ultimately, the program will progress to have participants walking, running and marathoning, yet teach along the way to eat properly both at home, work and school. Participants will eventually lead to run exotic marathons in locations like the Great Wall of China, Antarctica, the North Pole, Mt. Everest, Easter Island, Moscow, Grand Canyon, South Africa, Iceland, Dubai, etc. The program will in turn raise funds for obesity related research and promote educational awareness. "Do you or someone you know like to run, walk, or just like to take care of themselves?" Tim is looking for large corporate marketing, public relations or human resources leaders who would like to gain positive exposure for their organizations, or individuals who would like to learn more about Run 2 End Obesity.

Connect with Tim about Advanced Franchise Systems, PHresh Kitchen™, or Run 2 End Obesity at Tim@AdvancedFranchiseSystems.com; or Tim@PHreshKitchen.com; or Tim@TimothyPMurphy.com; or (407) 442-2695 for his office.

Richard Muscio

Richard Muscio CPA is "THE Family Office Guy." As a CPA with an estate/gift/trust background, Richard assists family offices (ultra-wealthy families) with estate and gift tax planning, family governance and succession planning, with the goal of helping wealthy families to thrive.

Richard speaks frequently on the topics of family governance, professional collaboration, business succession planning, business leaders as community leaders, and "The CPA Firm of the Future." You can view his presentations on these topics on his YouTube channel. He also hosts a weekly radio show *It's Your Money…and Your Life* (www.iymoney.com) on 760 AM KFMB, where he discusses wealth as being much more than just money.

Richard is co-author of *The Rise* with best-selling author Greg Reid. *The Rise* is about collaboration and never giving up on one's dreams. His next book, *So, What's Your Play? How Billie Jean, Bobby, and Blindness Begat Tolerance,* is scheduled for release in the summer of 2013 through Sherpa Press.

He is also co-founder of the Move Your Feet Before You Eat Foundation and the Oceanside Turkey Trot (www.osideturkeytrot.com). His foundation works to improve teen fitness and senior generation fitness in the Oceanside area, while encouraging family participation and community volunteerism. If you think you had a lot of people over for Thanksgiving, well, Richard hosted more than 9,000 runners and 14,000 people this past Thanksgiving morning in downtown Oceanside, raising over $ 100,000 for charities.

For fun, Richard is a long-distance endurance runner, having completed the 2012 Boston Marathon in record-breaking heat. Best of all, Richard is the father of Evan (22), Mia (21) and Demi (17) with his lovely wife Mari, who enjoys beating him in running events. Richard may be reached at rjm@ fabcpas.com.

Stacee Nelson

Throughout university and most of her twenties, Stacee worked as a social worker, caring for abused children, drug addicted teens and mentally ill adults. She was also actively involved in youth development and leadership programs. In 1999 she graduated from Thunderbird with an international MBA and joined the finance team at the European headquarters of an American Fortune 50 company. She spent the next 10 years working in strategic finance, business development, and mergers and acquisitions in Europe, and later in China, and traveling throughout Europe, Asia and Central America. In 2011 she started her own investment company dedicated to creating value for the American economy by turning distressed properties into jobs, homes, and investment opportunities. As an author, successful business owner, and philanthropist, she collaborates with other entrepreneurs to support and mentor business professionals to achieve their financial independence by having multiple streams of income.

She is based in Santa Barbara, CA and can be contacted at staceenelson.com, facebook/staceenelson.com or cashflowdivas.com

Carl Sheeler

Carl has enjoyed a twenty-five-year executive finance and operations career highlighted by the implementation of innovative ideas with solid metrics decreasing risk and increasing value while retaining stakeholder commitment. A problem solver, former Marine combat officer and a finance Ph.D. who has performed over a thousand midmarket, high profile litigation, valuation and restructuring engagements. He has assisted hundreds of business owners, family offices and private equity groups and their trusted advisors in creating over $4.5B of economic value in his capacity as the national managing partner of a 59-year-old business valuation and advisory services firm. He has testified 155 times on matters ranging from IRS taxpayer to shareholder disputes.

He is a national instructor of Great Distinction (NACVA) and an adjunct professor of finance, business and entrepreneurship. He has been a guest lecturer of the People's Republic of China where he presented on intangible asset values at the National Accounting Institute—Beijing and the Zhongnan University of Economics and Law in Wuhan. A prolific writer, he has contributed valuation chapters for the American Institute of Certified Public Accountants and the California Bar's Business Succession Manual. He has been cited in several authoritative texts and articles in valuation, legal and accounting journals.

A *Worth* magazine leading advisor, he has donated and helped raise commitments for over $2 million to help many philanthropic causes and serves as co-chair, SoCal Alliance of Mergers & Acquisition Advisors; the Business Advisory Board of the Point Loma Nazarene University Business School; the Editorial Advisory Board of the National Association of Certified Valuation Analysts; the YMCA's Planned Giving Advisory Board; the Rady Children's Hospital Foundation Estates & Trusts Executive Committee. He is the co-founder of the Strategic Trusted Advisor Roundtable ("STAR"), the Uber-Group and Privatus CI^{3}O Services, LLC. carl@bizvalsltd.com – 1-800-286-6635 x211 and www.linkedin.com/in/carlsheeler/

Erik Swanson

Speaker, trainer, author, motivator and success coach.

Erik Swanson has been changing lives all over the world with his innovative approach and proven method to teach you how to systematically change your habits and attitudes for the better. Erik has been delivering powerful trainings to corporations, associations, entrepreneurs, athletes, actors and business owners for the past fifteen years. His "Secret Habitudes" training system teaches you the amazing habit of developing an amazing attitude on a consistent basis. He brings you from where you are now, to where you really want to go in your life.

We are all habitual and he uses that to your advantage to move your growth curve. Change your habits, change your attitudes, change your lives! Allow Mr. Swanson to show you how to harness and maintain better habits and amazing attitudes each and every day of your life and become a Habitude Warrior.

For more information, visit www.HabitudeWarrior.com. You can reach Erik at BookErik@HabitudeWarrior.com and (888) 985-ERIK.

Monique Laurette Goffinet Tunney

Monique Laurette Goffinet Tunney is a creative communications professional that believes in creating ideas that really move a person and therefore people. Her career has been rich in both strategic and creative development, having over twenty years of experience in marketing and advertising, with the majority of her career being at FCB

Worldwide. During her tenure as a vice president, she was awarded Agency MVP for the development of brand building methodologies and development of a World Class Advertising educational seminar to understand creative problem solving and what it takes to inspire ideas that work. She was also presented with a Raise the Bar award for providing inspirational strategic and creative thinking.

As a self proclaimed "Swiss Army Knife," Monique Laurette continued her creative work with a small business she developed called, It's Art About You, initially creating personalized designs for personal and corporate gift giving. It's Art About You moved into advertising and communication strategy, as well as creative execution, tackling problems that require creative and strategic thinking, leading to brilliant solutions that feel like receiving the perfect gift.

Monique's purpose is to communicate the idea of SANTA (See Abundance Now Thankfully Always) in a spiritual way grounded in ethics and values rather than in religion—where all religions and human kindness come together in their emphasis on love, compassion, patience and tolerance. She is currently working on a way to share this idea, as well as help parents communicate this universal "magic" to their children. It is her mission to provide the tools to communicate the excitement of knowing that Santa is real in a much more powerful way than once thought of, and that we can all help keep this spirit very much alive. We can all become Santa, or "See Abundance Now Thankfully

Always," and teach our children this powerful idea that can aid in bringing the magic into their lives and into others. We really all can find a common ground and believe.

You can learn more about Monique Laurette Goffinet Tunney at www.artaboutyou.com and http://www.linkedin.com/in/moniquetunney. She can be reached at monique@artabout you.com.